Wacky, Wet,
and Wobbly

Wacky, Wet, *and* Wobbly

A Journey Through a Lifetime of Undiagnosed Hydrocephalus (Water on the Brain)

JEANNE G. DeBOLD

1603 Capitol Ave., Suite 310 Cheyenne, Wyoming USA 82001
1-888-980-6523 | admin@urlinkpublishing.com

URLink Print and Media is committed to excellence in the publishing industry.

Published in the United States of America

ISBN 978-1-64367-332-5 (Paperback)
ISBN 978-1-64367-333-2 (Digital)

Non-Fiction
28.03.19

* Thanks to Dr. Michael Holt, neurosurgeon on *A Gifted Man*, defunct television series, for giving me the title for my memoir.

This memoir is lovingly dedicated to my sister Barbara, my 'Guardian Angel'. Thank you for always being there for me.

CONTENTS

CHAPTER 1

The Million Dollar Question: What is Wrong With Me?!

*D*ear *Lord! I've fallen again! Why can't I get up off this blasted floor? Why won't my legs let me stand up? How can I be so weak and clumsy? Why is my life so out of control? Will my life always be so miserable? Why won't God be kind to me and end my life so I will no longer have to suffer this anguish?* I had asked myself those questions over and over again for the first fifty eight years of my lifetime.

My life has not been an easy one. It has been fraught with numerous trips and bad falls. But then again, are any falls really 'good' falls? I required countless surgeries to try to correct the damage done to my joints as a result of all those falls. If the sidewalk was just the slightest bit uneven, I would inevitably trip and fall headlong onto the pavement. I wiped out at the drop of a hat. I constantly tripped going UP the stairs (I would later learn the significance of this distinction) and would find myself sprawled all over the steps. Let me tell you–Humpty Dumpty could take lessons from me! I had so much practice that I surely knew how to fall with an inevitably new injury as a result. The problem was that sometimes I just couldn't get up again. *Strange ..... very strange .....*

From the time that I was a little girl, I always knew that there was something seriously wrong with me. I was plagued with obscure and seemingly unrelated signs and symptoms. I was never able to lie face down on my stomach without becoming exceedingly sick to my stomach or feeling as if I would pass out. If I tried to lie in a prone position, my vision would cloud over with white sparkling stars and my head would feel as if it was filling up with cotton. If I remained lying on my stomach, my vision would become absolutely white while I became exceedingly nauseated. The only way I could get up after lying on my stomach was to logroll onto my back and then I would have to sit up very, very slowly. It made getting a tan on my back very difficult when I was a young adult.

It got to the point where I found that these same miserable symptoms would occur even while I was seated. When this happened, I would have to shift the position of my spine in order to get the debilitating feelings under control. I frequently felt that my head was on the verge of exploding. I began living on aspirin in order to try to keep the headaches under control. But I soon realized that the aspirin didn't help—the 'headaches' would simply go away on their own with or without any intervention. They weren't really headaches at all—they were more intense feelings of unrelenting pressure in my skull. Really strange—but then I thought, so am I. No one else had these mysterious symptoms.

I discovered that I was unable to look over my head at anything up close. Those miserable feelings in my skull and stomach would return with a vengeance if I tried to do so. My balance was extremely poor and frequently when I fell, I was unable to get up. My legs would simply not support me. I suffered urinary incontinence while in my forties and had to wear *Depends* pads which I began buying in large quantities. I thought urinary incontinence was bad enough but then

I began suffering from occasional incontinence of stool in my early fifties. (Not fun and very humiliating!) Cleaning feces off white carpeting was not an easy task nor was it very pleasant, either.

I often found it difficult to find the word I was looking for when I was speaking to someone and just chalked it up to my being extremely introverted. Later in life, I frequently had difficulty following a simple conversation and actually thought that I perhaps had suffered a mild stroke. Balancing a checkbook soon became an impossibility for me.

But no one ever took me seriously when I tried to explain my problems. In early childhood, I quickly learned not to mention any of my issues and simply **soldiered on** throughout my lifetime. I felt that if I simply tried harder, I would be able to control my problem, whatever it was. I did my best to pretend that nothing was wrong. I did whatever I could do to the best of my ability but it was always such a struggle, such a monumental effort to do whatever everyone else seemed to do so very easily. I pretended that nothing was wrong but little did I know that there was definitely something very, very wrong with me. It would take over a half century to discover what my problem was and what needed to be done to finally correct it.

Here is the story of my mysterious affliction .....

CHAPTER 2

The Early Years

Where should I begin? Ah, yes, the beginning would be the most logical place to start, would it not?

I remember as a very young child, watching that new-fangled invention called 'television' with my best friend, Gale. She always had the newest dolls, the best toys, and now her family had a television too! I was so envious. It seemed like she had everything I didn't have. All she had to do was ask her mother for something and poof!!! ….. There it was! She had this really beautiful dollhouse made out of tin. The roof came off so you could put your dolls inside. The dollhouse was even completely furnished! We spent many fun-filled hours playing with that dollhouse.

I remember being amazed that my friend's mother actually knew how to drive a car! I always felt so important when we rode up to school, chauffeured in a turquoise blue '57 Chevrolet Impala! You remember, the car with those flashy tail fins! And her family had not just one car but two! But the object of my envy just now was not their cars. *Gale had a television set!*

Why can't we have a television too, Daddy? How come I don't have a real Barbie doll like Gale has? Why do I have to have an imitation Barbie from John's Bargain Store, I pleaded to my father. My sisters and I were much loved in our home and we had all the basic necessities. But we didn't have all the creature comforts and luxuries that many of our friends had. My father would simply say, *We can't afford them. You have a roof over your head and food on the table. You should learn to be grateful for that.*

My father was a loving but strict parent who probably invented the concept of 'tough love'. He would try to look so stern but there was always a hint of a smile at the corners of his mouth when he was meting out our very rare discipline. He didn't fool me! He was also a very hardworking man. He worked two jobs all throughout my childhood. If he had had the opportunity to continue his education, I know he would have been a very fine doctor. As it was, he was a scale mechanic who worked for his own father in Grandpa's scale repair shop in Brooklyn, New York (*Yeah! Brooklyn!* It seems as if you always have to say that whenever you say 'Brooklyn.')

Anyway, my father never had the opportunity to continue his education after he graduated from high school. After all, he had a wife and three daughters to support. He taught me many valuable life lessons which have gotten me through some very rough periods in my lifetime. I think the most important lesson he instilled in me was how to handle finances. I learned how to make do with whatever I had at the moment and to always save for the future. My dad firmly believed in those rainy days ahead! Even though we had very little money growing up, we never had any serious wants (except for maybe that television!). My father took the train from Long Island to Brooklyn every day and I remember that he would put two dollars on the refrigerator so my mother could get food for supper. (I can hear you exclaim, "Two dollars?! Only two dollars?" Remember, this was when a loaf of Wonder white bread cost fifteen cents and you could get a pound of ground round for fifty nine cents. Yeah, so okay, I'm that old!)

My father also instilled a very strong work ethic in me. If I'm not doing something productive, I generally feel very guilty. My father also taught me to take great pride in whatever I'm doing. He always said, "If a job is worth doing, then it's worth doing well!"

My mother was a housewife who deep down in her heart really wanted to be an artist. If it involved her hands, she could do it all and she could do it well–she crocheted, knitted, did ceramics, as well as crewelwork and needlepoint. However, the most impressive thing she did was oil painting. Her portraits and seascapes were museum-quality work. Her very impressive portrait of General Westmoreland still hangs proudly in our home. Her hands were magical.

She was a very kind, soft-spoken woman who always had a word of encouragement. She was a very forgiving person who tried to instill in us the value of others. Considering that she was brought up in a very prejudiced era, she never spoke disparagingly of any minority. Everyone was equal in her eyes. I learned my sense of tolerance from her. Bigotry was not written in her dictionary.

Ahh, but I digress. I need to point out the significance of watching television with my friend that fateful day. It was a pivotal event in my life. I suddenly realized that I wasn't able to lie on my stomach like she did. She was lying face down with her legs flying up in the air over her back. When I tried to copy her pose, my vision clouded over with vast whiteness, I became nauseated, and my head started to pound as if it was going to explode! It felt as if my skull was being stuffed full of very white cotton and I could no longer see anything but vast and brilliant whiteness. I was terrified! I panicked because I thought that perhaps I was suddenly going blind.

Even at that young age, I knew that I was close to passing out. As my vision clouded over with occluding whiteness, I began to see brilliant multi-colored stars which were actually kind of pretty. The only way I was able to sit upright was to roll over onto my back. I had to lie there for a while as it took several moments for that horrible feeling in my head and stomach to subside. I really didn't want to vomit on Gale's living room rug. That would have been rather embarrassing.

When she saw that I was having a problem, Gale became alarmed. I told her what had happened and asked her if that happened to her as well. She looked at me rather strangely and said, "No, of course not! You're just being silly! Come on! Let's go outside and play!" I would come to know that strange look of disbelief over the course of my lifetime on the few occasions when I got up the courage to tell someone of my difficulty. However, because of their disbelieving reaction, I quickly learned not to discuss my peculiar symptoms with anyone. It was a secret that I thought I would have to carry to my grave.

When I went home that day, I told my mother what had happened. Being my mom, she didn't look at me with that strange look of disbelief. As I said, she was a very tolerant and compassionate person. She knew that I wouldn't make something like that up just to get attention. So, my parents bundled me up and took me off to see our family doctor.

After I told him what had happened, he too gave me that strange look of disbelief that I had seen on my best friend's face. He had me lie on my stomach and, sure enough, I became nauseated and my head started filling up with cotton again. I felt as though I was going to vomit but I tried very hard to maintain some semblance of calm despite my terrifying feelings of panic. *This isn't right! Something is wrong with me!* I wanted to shout to him. But being the good little girl that I was, I didn't say a word in my defense. I always kept quiet and tried very hard never to say anything wrong or do anything that would upset anyone. Although my discomfort was obvious to the doctor, he was not very sympathetic at all. I remember how he just shook his head and scowled.

His comment to me was, "Well, if lying on your stomach makes you feel ill, then don't lie on your stomach!" He never suggested that any tests be done to try to find out the cause of my difficulty. He just dismissed me as a child who liked to make up stories to get attention. He told my parents that there was nothing wrong with me and to just ignore my complaints and, more importantly, to ignore me as well! My parents and I never discussed my problem again even when I was an adult. We simply swept it under the carpet and pretended that nothing was wrong. After all, if you don't admit that you have a problem, then you don't have to try to do anything to correct it. Ignorance is indeed bliss but, believe me, I was anything but blissful.

Looking back on it, I guess it was a very strange complaint and the doctor probably had no clue as to what the cause of my difficulty could possibly be. And actually, the test that would finally diagnose my problem had not yet even been invented or even thought about. He was just a very simple country doctor who was good for colds and sore throats but certainly nothing any more serious than that. However, his thoughtless remark that day formed the basis of all of my self-doubt and self-recriminations throughout my entire lifetime. It is amazing how someone's words said so casually can stay with you for years and years, words that the person probably doesn't even remember having said them.

I learned throughout my lifetime to follow that doctor's harsh advice. I simply ignored the symptoms and tried to do the best I could at the time. After all, he said there was nothing wrong with me, right? I also made sure that I hid my difficulty from everyone around me. I had decided that to admit to my problem was to admit to being weak and I was determined to never show any signs of weakness.

Soldier on .....

I remember with much shame and embarrassment that I was a bed-wetter. There, I said it. It's hard to admit that but it's a very cold (or warm!) and harsh reality. Despite my Mom's best efforts, my bedroom always reeked of urine. I would never go on sleep-overs because I knew exactly what would happen. I didn't want to be embarrassed in front of my friends. One year just before Halloween, I so much wanted a Bugs Bunny costume so I could look really cool when I went trick-or-treating. My mother told me that if I didn't wet the bed that night, she would get it for me even though we didn't have any extra money that week. I'm ashamed to say that I never did get that costume. Since my two older sisters never had this problem, my Mom didn't know quite how to handle my difficulty. She didn't realize that a child with enuresis is physiologically unable to control the release of urine during sleep. No amount of effort on the part of the sufferer could prevent the passage of urine during sleep. I wasn't trying to be a willful or difficult child. I simply could not help it.

She felt that if I tried very hard that I could simply overcome the problem on my own. I guess that's where I got the belief that I was always incredibly weak. Of course, I felt that I was responsible for my actions and if I just put in some effort, I wouldn't wet the bed anymore. But, oh dear, no matter how hard I tried, I always woke up to a bed saturated with urine. It's only now that I realize that my urinary incontinence then was most likely due to the bigger problem that I would have to deal with all my life. Urinary frequency and incontinence would rear their ugly heads throughout most of my adult life. Finding restrooms wherever I went became second nature to me. I could tell you where they were located in every store that I patronized because I would have to find them in a hurry or I would have urine streaming down my legs!

Oh, but wetting the bed was only a minor problem. No matter how hard I tried (and believe me, I tried!), I could never seem to keep my feet beneath me. My balance was practically non-existent. I would fall over at the drop of a hat. Because of my balance problems, I was constantly falling on the playground. My knees were always covered with bloody scabs in various stages of healing. My mother used to say that she should take out stock in *Band-Aids!* If she did, she said we'd be millionaires, thanks to me!

I remember when I was being confirmed that my right knee was badly torn up from yet another fall. (*Oh, that poor right knee! What a beating it took throughout my entire lifetime!*) When the Bishop was blessing us, we were expected to kneel. My knee hurt so badly but the nun said, *You must kneel, Jeanne. He's the Bishop and you will show your respect! Kneel!!* She ominously slapped that ruler in her hand and I knew that she meant business. Being the good little girl that I was, I knelt the whole time that was required. When I got up, my knee was bleeding through the *Band-Aid* and blood was dripping down my leg. I always seemed to have blood or urine running down my leg. But I did what I was supposed to do then and I still do.

CHAPTER 3

The Teenage Years

When I was a teenager, I absolutely adored the television show, *The Man from U.N.C.L.E.* I guess my poor beleaguered father just couldn't stand listening to three girls whining all the time! He finally relented and had gotten us a fifteen-inch *Dumont* television. A *Dumont*! Wow! We were really in the big times now! Being the incredibly handy man that he was, my father made a very impressive cabinet for it.

We could now watch all those shows that our friends watched and we'd talk about them as if the characters were our very own personal friends. *Did you see Allison kissing Rodney last night on* Peyton Place? *That was some hot kiss! What do you think Rodney's brother is going to do now??!!* My sisters were so happy! But me, not so much. My strange problem had not gone away and I was still plagued by feelings and worries that I believed I could not discuss with anyone, especially my family. I never wanted to appear weak so I just kept it all bottled up inside me.

I can remember watching the coming attractions for *The Man from U.N.C.L.E.* one particular week. I remember praying, *Dear God, please let me live long enough to see* The Man from U.N.C.L.E. *next week. It really looks so good! Please don't let me die before then.* That was how much I was affected by my problem, whatever it was. Later in life, I found myself praying to God, not that I would live, but rather that He would please let me die so I wouldn't have to go through this misery anymore. After my retirement, I found that I no longer had the desire or the ability to **soldier on**. Oh, but I'm jumping ahead of myself, aren't I? Let's go back to my teenage years once again.

Maybe it was only a 1950's Long Island thing but do you remember that when it was your birthday, a girl would wear a big bow on her shoulder? You would attach certain items to the bow to signify your age. I remember my mom attaching Life Savers, lollipops, bubble gum, dog biscuits (since I never thought of myself as being pretty, I always resented the dog biscuit year!), and sugar cubes for Sweet Sixteen. I don't think you can even get those big sugar cubes anymore, just those tiny dots of compressed sugar. As you walked down the hallways at school, everyone would wish you a 'Happy Birthday'. Okay, so that was a good memory. I guess there were some fun times, after all–it wasn't just misery but the bad times because of my problem definitely outweighed the good times.

High school was not always a barrel of laughs for me, however. One day, while sitting with my friends in the high school cafeteria, I recall that we somehow got around to debating how long we each thought we'd live. One friend said, *Oh, eighty years at least.* Another said, *A hundred!* Since I made sure that I never discussed my 'weird' problem, my friends were totally oblivious to the difficulties I faced each and every day. They looked rather askance at me when I said, *I doubt that I'll live past the age of thirty five. As a matter of fact, I hope I don't live any longer than that.* When they demanded to know my reason for making such an absurd statement, I brushed them off and refused to explain. Why bother? They wouldn't believe me anyway. No one ever believed me so I just kept my mouth shut as I continued to struggle through each and every day.

Soldier on .....

Gym class in high school was a nightmare for me. Because of my balance issue, I was not able to walk across the balance beam. Can you just imagine? I was an A student who nearly failed gym because of my inability to simply walk across that blasted beam. Everyone else sailed across it with no problem. They could do back flips and pirouettes on that beam and I wasn't even able to just walk across it, even if I went very, very slowly. As usual, I was so envious of anyone who could do something that I couldn't do. No matter how hard I tried, I would always fall off halfway down the length of the beam. But I tried! Lord help me, I really did my very best but as usual, it was not good enough, I was not good enough. I guess my gym teacher took pity on me because she finally gave me a passing grade in physical education, the only D I ever received in high school. At least, I passed. Whew!! That was close. How would I have ever been able to explain to my parents that I had failed gym because I wasn't able to walk across the balance beam??!! That would probably have forced us to discuss my problem but I wasn't willing to go there. Best to let sleeping dogs lie.

There was another television show that was very popular during my teenage years. It was about a brooding neurosurgeon who was very serious and never, ever smiled. I remember the opening of that show. Sam Jaffe would intone, "Man, Woman, Life, Death, Infinity". They just don't write shows like that anymore! In every episode, _Ben Casey_ would soon discover that everyone he met had a brain tumor or at least an acute subdural hematoma and that they required immediate brain surgery to save their lives. So melodramatic! I would often think that perhaps my problem was a brain tumor. *Hey, Ben Casey, why don't you come and see me? I could be another one of your success stories!* Ahh, well, I knew that would never happen. I was absolutely certain that no one could ever help me. It took over a half century to finally find the cause of all my problems. I wasn't so far off in thinking that it was a brain tumor! My difficulty was certainly centered in my brain but it wasn't a malignant brain tumor. No, it was something very different but just as serious.

CHAPTER 4

Off to College

I remember in high school that I had decided that I was going to go away to college to become a primary school teacher. My father was very old-fashioned and he told me that I should work in Woolworth's (remember that great five and dime store?? You could get anything and everything there from penny candy that actually cost a penny [what a concept!] to a pair of Buster Brown shoes). My father said that while I was working there, I would meet a man, get married, and have children. I knew that there was something more out there for me. So, since I planned on taking out loans to pay for my own college tuition, I told my father that I was indeed going to go to college. He finally capitulated but then the argument became, "You'll go to a local college and commute!" Well, I knew that going away to school was half of the college experience and I wanted to 'find myself'. This was the Sixties, after all.

After a few battles royale, I finally went away to college with the hope of becoming a grade school teacher. I soon discovered that teaching would not be possible for me due to my difficulty, whatever it was. I had always admired my second grade teacher and so I wanted to teach that grade. But

I soon found out that so much of the school day was spent on the floor with the children. I discovered to my dismay that I was unable to get up off the floor, no matter how hard I tried. My legs would just not lift me up. Once again, I blamed myself for being incredibly weak. Since I knew that I would be doomed to be a failure if I tried to be a teacher, I changed my major to Liberal Arts with a minor in Psychology. I didn't think that mental health care workers spent any time on the floor with their patients so I figured that might be a safer career choice.

At college, I finally told my closest friends about my 'weird' problem. One friend was especially supportive and encouraged me to try to find out the cause of the issue. He knew me well and cared a great deal about me. He didn't give me that strange look of disbelief when I told him of my issue.

I had an E.E.G. done while I was at college. Much to my dismay, it didn't show anything conclusive and certainly did not explain any of the symptoms from which I had been suffering. Now I had actual concrete proof that there was nothing really wrong with me. I took in a deep breath of disappointment. I had hoped that this test would show something, anything, to prove that there really was cause for concern. I foolishly believed that something would be discovered and that all of my misery was explainable by a physical problem. But since the test showed that there was nothing physiologically wrong with me, I once again had to accept the fact that all of my problems were just a figment of my imagination.

I guess that doctor in my childhood was right. I am just making it all up. So, as usual, I tried to ignore the problems and continued to do the best I could at the time. I learned to accept what I could do and also what I couldn't do. I tried very hard to hide my problems. But being a very stubborn German (*Thank you, Dad!*), I refused to let anyone see the hardship I was enduring or the problems that I was having just getting through each and every day. I simply continued to struggle with all my might to do the things that everyone else could do so easily. Oh, how I envied them! *Why can't I be like them?* I lamented.

Soldier on .....

CHAPTER 5

Star Trek

Since I was somewhat limited in what I was able to do physically, I continued to find great comfort in television. It was during my freshman year at college that the first episode of **Star Trek** aired on September 8, 1966. That episode, *The Man Trap*, took me in hook, line, and sinker. I was absolutely enthralled and very impressed with the sophistication of this series. To see three men who really loved each other and cared about one another (*No, not that way! Get your mind out of the gutter!*) was so heart-warming. The main theme of the show was that there is always hope for the future and that we can get through anything if we work together as a team. To this day, some sixty plus years later, my heart still trills when I hear those first four musical notes, see the stars whizzing by on a black backdrop as the French horns take up the cause, and William Shatner intones these iconic words:

> *Space, a final frontier -*
> *These are the voyages of the Starship Enterprise.*
> *Its five year mission, to explore strange new worlds,*
> *to seek out new life and new civilizations,*
> *to boldly go where no man has gone before.* ©

I would lose myself in those thrilling adventures. My problem had certainly not abated when I went off to college; if anything, it made its presence known more acutely. Each day continued to be a struggle to just get by. I knew that all Bones McCoy, Chief Medical Officer of the *Enterprise*, would have to do was wave his medical scanner over me and the answer to my crippling symptoms would easily be found and all would be well in my universe. I was actually correct in that assumption. It would take a very special kind of scanner to finally diagnose my problem but that was years in the future–my future, that is, not **Star Trek**'s.

I began to toy with the idea of writing a **Star Trek** novel. It would take me many years, however, to finally come up with a premise and the time to devote to writing a full length novel. But I did! Three times, actually! More on that later .....

CHAPTER 6

My Days as a Psychiatric Social Worker

Having been a product of college in the 1960's, I believed that I could make a real difference to the world if I became a social worker. I was determined to right all wrongs, see that the world achieved social equality, and I would banish poverty. Worldwide hunger would be eliminated and children would receive the education that they deserved. I had, after all, participated in several peace demonstrations while I was in college. I wore bellbottom jeans and love beads. I was truly a hippie and proud of it! The Vietnam War was still dragging on at this time and I, along with my fellow countrymen, watched the bloody conflict unfold in gory detail every evening during the dinner hour news.

Just before my senior year in college ended, the Kent State killings occurred. In order to avoid demonstrations on campus, the administration decided to give the students a choice: they could either accept the grade they currently had in their courses and leave campus immediately or else they could remain on campus and do research papers to improve their present grade. All classes were immediately cancelled. Much of the campus became deserted with no more music ringing out over the hills. There was a very somber tone to the school as we mourned those who were killed at Kent State and all those thousands who died so needlessly in Southeast Asia.

I hated the thought of college ending and so I elected to remain on campus. I did lengthy research papers and 'partied hearty' in between visits to the library. I had really been very pleased with my grades but decided to improve them anyway. I actually wound up with straight A's that semester in courses that were very difficult. Just before I left campus, I realized that I really wasn't feeling all that well–listless, tired all the time, no appetite. I just chalked it up to too many all-nighters (and parties!) in a row and went about my business as best I could. But then, that's what I always did.

By the time I got home from school, I became very ill with mononucleosis. The doctor who diagnosed it was actually the same one who had told me that there was nothing wrong with me when I was unable to lie on my stomach. My first summer home was spent in bed, barely able to take a shower without collapsing. I was really a very sick puppy.

When I was finally well enough, I began pounding the pavement for a social worker position. I was fortunate enough to become the medical social worker at an exclusive private psychiatric hospital very near my home. (Notice I said that I became their medical social worker. No matter what you may think, I was not a patient!). I really enjoyed my work there and the administration soon took note of me. I was promoted to Admissions Officer and one of my duties required that I take an in-depth anamnesis or history of every patient.

Once a month, I had to work the four p.m. to midnight shift and so I had my mornings free that weekend. I enjoyed horseback riding and went for my usual lesson one Saturday morning. The horse I was riding was spooked if he was taken out on the trails. He began bucking and the instructor told me to hang on since the horse had to learn to ride the trails. I screamed, "Not with me on him!" I was able to hang on for three huge bucks but finally lost my seating on the fourth rearing up. I went down to the ground, twisting my body in mid-air in order to avoid landing on a huge stump! My right elbow was at a rather peculiar angle and the riding instructor immobilized my arm in a magazine! I was taken to the hospital in a police car. I remember asking the officer if I could play with his siren! He laughed and said, "I guess you're all right."

Well, my right elbow was dislocated. The orthopedic surgeon told me I'd have to be admitted if they had to give me anesthesia. No way was I going to be admitted so I said, "Just do it!" He pulled on my arm until the bone went back into place. Ouch!!! Boy, did that hurt! But the pain was only momentary and I was used to dealing with discomfort. My arm was encased in a big plaster cast and I gulped when I realized that I wouldn't be able to drive to work (I drove a standard shift.) I called my supervisor, who I was told jumped on his desk when he heard me tell him that I'd be out for a while! Since I was the only one at the hospital who had been trained to do anamneses, he arranged for a chauffeur-driven limousine to bring me to work every day. I used a Dictaphone to record my notes and a secretary transcribed my histories. I felt pretty privileged—and special! I wonder what the neighbors thought when that fancy black car drove up to my home every morning. The chauffeur opened my door and made sure that I comfortable. Nice .....

When the psychiatric hospital opened a brand new nursing home, I was asked to become the Admissions Officer for that facility. I really flourished there and greatly enjoyed my work. A receptionist there would page me, saying, "Miss De ..... Bold." Soon, everyone was calling me "Misty" which I kind of liked.

Anyway, I had been having a lot of symptoms from my condition and I actually told a few people at the hospital about them. It was an in-patient psychiatric hospital after all with lots of neurologists on staff. I recall that I told the receptionist what would happen if I tried to lie on my stomach. I jokingly imitated the way it would affect me and put my head down on my desk. She panicked and said, "My God! Are you all right?!" When I lifted my head off the desk and she saw that I was smiling, she said, "Don't you dare ever do that to me again! I thought I had to call an emergency!"

I half-heartedly told one of the doctors there about my difficulties and he suggested that I have another E.E.G. performed. (I think he was more interested in doing a research paper on me than on finding the cause of my problem.) I reluctantly agreed to have the test. *Maybe this time they'll actually find something.* No such luck!

I had icky paste and lots of wires attached to my head. What a morning that was! As usual, the test wasn't very conclusive. There was some 'slowing' in the brainwave pattern and the doctor said that I had simply fallen asleep. I knew that I hadn't slept at all during the test. Even though there was nothing conclusive in the results, the doctor unenthusiastically said he could do exploratory open-brain surgery for possible cancer. Where was *Ben Casey* when I needed him?!

Gulp??!! *You want to saw my skull open?* That sounded pretty serious. I wasn't sure if I was ready for something that drastic especially since nothing conclusive had shown up on the E.E.G. I put the neurosurgeon on hold while I considered the possibility. As usual, I went on with my life pretending that nothing was wrong. But deep down in my heart, I knew better. But open-brain surgery??!! I couldn't face that ..... I don't think I ever told my parents about the possibility. I didn't want to worry them.

Soldier on .....

CHAPTER 7

Kung Fu

It was during the time that I was working at the nursing home that the television show *Kung Fu* had become very popular. My sister Barbara and I decided that we'd take up this very inscrutable martial art. My sister's friend worked with a *kung fu* master and so we thought we'd try his studio.

Tonny, our *Shifu* or master, held a black belt in the sport and could break five boards at once with one hand. He would lie on a bed of very sharp nails, his assistant would put a board over his stomach, and then his assistant would use a sledge hammer to break the board over *Shifu's* stomach. *Whack!!!* Tonny would grin and walk away with nary a drip of blood on his back. He was really amazing. When we asked him how he did that, he said that it was all in the mind. (Hmmm ….. sounds a lot like Spock from **Star Trek**…..)

We practiced the exercise forms of various animals–snake, crane, monkey, and dragon and, in the process, became quite proficient at self defense. Balance was always a problem for me but I managed to get through it. I somehow seemed to be able to compensate for the fact that I wasn't able to hold a one-footed pose for more than two seconds. I tried to make up for my lack of balance with brute strength.

Not only did Tonny, who became a very good friend, teach us the beauty and deadliness of *kung fu*, he also taught us about the Chinese culture. Prior to this, the only so-called Chinese food I had ever eaten was Chun King chow mein out of a can. *Bleck!!!* But with Tonny's superb cooking skills, I soon savored the taste of homemade wontons, hot and sour soup, and real Kung Pao chicken. Tonny didn't drink alcohol except for an occasional beer <u>on ice</u>! We were at a party at his house one hot summer's afternoon and Tonny was making up a punch. He poured <u>whole liters</u> of rum, gin, and vodka into some fruit juice. Man, those were the best Mai Tai's I ever had! Hiccup!

Tonny was given an old beat up *papier-mâché* lion (it actually looks like a dragon). He wanted us to do the lion dance during demonstrations. Well, Barbara and I brought that poor lion back from the brink of extinction. With tender loving care, we were able to restore it to his former beauty. Tonny very proudly included the lion dance in all of our demonstrations after that resurrection.

I was quite amazed when I was able to break two boards at one time. *Shifu* Tonny was right–it's all in the mind set. Our arms and legs were always black and blue from all the 'combat' we did. We fought our classmates like mortal enemies during practice but we were the best of friends outside of class. I never met a more congenial and homogenous group of people as those who studied with us. Ahh, yes, those were good times.

When you really get into the practice of martial arts, it begins to take over your thoughts and actions. You want to walk around with hundred dollar bills hanging out of your pocket just so you could maybe use some moves against any would-be thieves. Actually, *Shifu* Tonny made it very clear that we were only to use the art as a form of exercise and to use it only in self-defense if our safety was being threatened.

We were taught to try to walk away from any confrontation and to always use peaceful means to get out of any difficulty. We were only to use the art if our life or someone else's life or well-being was in jeopardy.

That having been said, I have to admit that there was one time that I might not have followed *Shifu* Tonny's admonition. I was casually strolling in the aisles of a supermarket one day when a friend, who knew I was studying *kung fu*, sneaked up behind me and grabbed my shoulder hard! Without even thinking, I swung around, picked him right up off his feet and pinned him up against the Campbell's tomato soup! When I realized who it was, we both had a good laugh! But let me tell you, he never sneaked up on me again! He was no fool!

Looking back on my life, I now realize that whenever I was physically active, my mysterious ailment did not present that much of a problem for me. If I had realized this back then, I would have made sure that I had been physically active at all times. But then again, hindsight is always twenty-twenty, isn't it?

Despite the euphoria of seeming to be able to put my 'weird' symptoms on the back burner while studying *kung fu*, I began to have more difficulties again, especially severe headaches. Well, not really headaches—more a feeling that my head was filling up to the point where I thought it would explode.

It was at this time that I had been working at the private psychiatric hospital. I had had the second E.E.G. which had not been very conclusive about any problem. However, the surgeon had half-heartedly suggested doing open-brain surgery to see if there was any explanation of my difficulties. When I told *Shifu* Tonny that I was considering brain surgery, he showed me several exercises that I would need to do to keep up my skill level. His world was *kung fu* and he didn't want to see one of his disciples, albeit a rather mediocre one, lose her enthusiasm. *But Shifu, they want to crack my skull open?!* He calmly replied, *You'll be okay. Just do these exercises and you'll be back with us in no time.*

After giving the possibility of brain surgery some additional thought, I decided not to go there. Since I had had this condition all my life, I knew that in all likelihood that I did not have cancer and that was the only possibility that the surgeon had suggested. I had no idea that all of my symptoms, not just the 'headaches', were related so I decided against that option and went not-so merrily on my way.

Soldier on .....

CHAPTER 8

Our Day of Independence

In 1976, the two hundredth birthday of our country, my family and I decided that we wanted to move to the country. When I gave my notice at the nursing home where I worked on Long Island, I remember my boss saying that he would send a helicopter for me so I could continue working there. He didn't want me to leave and I think he may have been serious in his offer! Nice memory.

It took us a long time but we finally found a beautiful home in a little town in upstate New York. We had decided to move in gradually and so went up to our new home every weekend. We had about two acres of land which was huge, considering that we had only had a small lot on Long Island. My sister and I decided to plant a vegetable garden. We were so thrilled when we came up one time to see vegetable plants actually sprouting from the earth! We had never had any success in growing much of anything on Long Island as the soil was too sandy.

I remember I was heading off to work one morning and I asked my father what he planned to do that day. "Oh, I think I'll straighten out the barn." So, I thought he meant that he was going to do some cleaning. No so!! When I came home from work that day, I realized that the barn, which had been very lop-sided and on the verge of collapse, was now straight as an arrow! I exclaimed, "How did you do that??!!" He shrugged his shoulders and said, "Pulleys and winches." He didn't have any help from anyone and so he did it all by himself. Like I said, he was amazing and so very talented.

Another amazing thing during this time was that my mother began making Easter eggs. You know, those decorated sugar eggs with little scenes in the cut-out end. She began making them to order. You could have any color or scene you wanted. I remember that despite our best efforts, we couldn't keep the kitchen floor from being sticky during the two months before Easter. And how much sugar we went through! Like I said, her hands were magical. I still have two eggs she made for me. They're all faded and some of the Royal icing has fallen off but I will never throw them away. They hold a place of honor on my bookshelf every Easter.

I began working at a nursing home about a thirty minute drive from my parents' home in upstate New York until I finally got my own apartment very near to where I was working. I provided emotional support and referral services to patients and their families. I became very attached to many of the residents there and felt as if I was doing good and important work.

The medical social worker position at the community hospital became available and I was pleased to have been given the opportunity. I worked very closely with Fran, a great nurse there with whom I still maintain contact. Here, I was at the other end of the referral process. My main duties included getting patients into local nursing homes. Trying to convince a recalcitrant patient that s/he was no longer able to live alone at home was sometimes very difficult.

"But what will become of Fluffy?" one lady exclaimed.

"Won't your family take your cat?" I asked.

"No, they're all allergic to cats and besides Fluffy will only come to me! I can't leave her!"

Knowing that the cat would wind up at the animal shelter broke my heart as well as my patient's. Hard choices had to be made but I helped my patients as best I could but I was beginning to feel very sad in my work.

It was during this time of rather bleak days that I decided to spend my spare time writing a book based on the *Star Trek* series. I was still enamored with that show that was so uplifting and hopeful for the future. I was certainly feeling very pessimistic about my life at this point due to my unhappy duties at work and also because of the difficulties I faced each and every day due to my mysterious condition.

Losing myself in the adventures of *Star Trek* was the best therapy I could have had. I was able to forget some of my worries and concerns for a while during my writing sessions. I was finally able to write a short novel based on the original television series. This was during the days of typewriters and carbon paper! I learned that you had to type a manuscript double-spaced with your name at the top of each page. If there was a typo, your manuscript would be tossed into the junk heap, no matter how good it was! I made a half-hearted attempt at getting it published but soon just put it on the shelf to gather dust, all but forgotten until the days of my retirement. More on *Star Trek* to follow .....

Losing myself in *Star Trek* was helpful but I realized that I had to do some very serious thinking about my professional life. Being around people who were always in crisis had begun to take its toll on me. The song 'Tomorrow' from "*Annie*" became a mantra for me. I was wondering if the sun would ever make an appearance in my life. I had begun to realize that I was just going through the motions in my job which wasn't fair to my patients, my employer, or me. I knew I had to make a change but it was so easy to just try to get through each day at work. The final straw that brutally forced me to make a decision about leaving the field of social work came when I had to interview a five-year old girl who had been sexually molested by her mother's scumbag of a boyfriend. I thought, *That's it! I don't want to see the dark side of life anymore! Even though I'm getting the highest salary I've ever had and I'm getting great benefits, this is just not the best field for me anymore. There's got to be sunshine and happiness out there somewhere but I'll certainly not find it if I stay in this line of work.*

When I was in high school, I had worked summers at a bakery and I LOVED it! I worked the morning shift (5:30 a.m.!) and knew what every customer wanted before he even opened his mouth! I decided that I would go back to school and learn how I could open my own bakery. That's quite a career change, don't you think?! But then again, I've never done anything half-heartedly. I've always been an all or nothing type of person.

CHAPTER 9

Off to Hotel Technology School

So, I dipped into my savings and enrolled in a school in the Catskills to study hotel technology. I really blossomed there. It felt so good to be so happy all the time. Don't get me wrong–it was a tremendous amount of work, especially since I was cramming two years of courses into one year. We had to memorize all of the recipes for the dishes that we had to prepare. I learned how to bake and cook in large quantities. To this day, I only know how to prepare food for the Ninth Regiment! Cooking for only two people seems to be beyond me. I learned the proper way to serve and clear a table. We had to 'cap' ashtrays by putting a clean ashtray over a filled ashtray after there was only one cigarette butt in the ashtray. Obviously, this was during the days before smoking was prohibited in dining rooms. I learned how to tend bar and how to mix cocktails. I loved all of my classes and professors with one exception.

My professor in Purchasing was extremely boring but it was a required course so I thought I'd just muddle through it. I knew I wasn't learning anything that would benefit me in my desire to open a bakery.

Then one day, he showed us some slides. "This is an apple," he droned. *Yikes,* I thought. *Did he just tell me that that was an apple? He didn't even tell us the variety of apple, just simply that it was an apple?! Does he really think we're that stupid??!!* I heard the kids in my class groan right along with me. Well, the professor forgot something in his office. While he was gone, I stood up and said, "I don't know about you guys but I think this class is a joke! I'm paying for this out of my own pocket and I can't afford to waste my money. I am going to go to the head of the Hotel Technology Department tomorrow and tell him what I think about this professor. How do you feel about it?"

Well, you would have thought I'd thrown a steak to a starving man!

Everyone stood up and started applauding, many of them saying, "Let me go with you!" Remember, I was thirty years old at this point and all of the other students were late teens or twenty somethings. I chose two students to go with me.

The following morning, I respectfully requested an appointment with the head of the department. When he found out the reason for my request, I was astonished when he cleared his calendar for me late that morning. One of the students who was going with me was a bit of a hot head. I warned him to be quiet and to let me do the talking. Since I was kind of a mother figure, he readily agreed which rather shocked me.

The head of the department was absolutely elated that I had brought this to his attention. He had been hearing grumblings over the years about this particular professor but no one would come forward to lodge an official complaint. Therefore, there was nothing he could do about it. I said, "Well, we're coming forward and we're formally logging a complaint. What can we do about this?"

It was a tricky situation since this professor had tenure. "I'll send the other professors in the department to sit in on his classes and we'll take it from there."

My Kitchen Operations professor and I had developed a really good relationship. Since I was older than the other students, he had a great deal of respect for me as I had for him. As with most chefs in the business, he commanded instant respect. Let me tell you that when he told you to jump, you loudly said, "Yes, Chef! How high?!"

He was very angry that I had leveled this complaint against my Purchasing professor. "He's been here for so many years. He's a great teacher. How could you cause all these problems for him? It's not fair." He changed his tune, however, when he sat in on one of the Purchasing professor's classes. "You were really right, Jeanne. He used to be a wonderful professor. Kids learned so much from him over the years. I don't know what's changed."

Unfortunately, this Purchasing professor was the only teacher of color in the Hotel Technology division. Pretty soon, the NAACP paid a visit to campus! But there's a very happy ending to all of this. Although he had loved teaching years ago, it seems that this professor had become very bored with the classroom. His dream had always been to open up a restaurant of his own but he just got in a rut and didn't do anything about it. Last I heard, he had opened up a restaurant that is thriving and he's as happy as a Clams Casino! The other teachers in the division took over his classes for the rest of the semester and I actually learned a lot about Purchasing over and above, "This is an apple".

CHAPTER 10

Happy at a Resort

One very important lesson I learned at my Hotel Technology school was that it is very difficult for a business to survive in the hospitality field. Just by serving one extra pat of butter with each meal, a restaurant can actually go bankrupt. I also realized that I didn't have the capital necessary to open my own bakery so I soon gave up that dream. However, I had really enjoyed my time at Hotel Technology school and I definitely wanted to work in the hospitality field in some capacity.

I graduated with top honors in my class and won several awards for outstanding achievement in various areas. With my Hotel Technology degree firmly in hand, I once again pounded the pavement. My search was very brief (actually, I landed the first position for which I applied). I proudly went to work at the Interlaken Inn, a very exclusive resort in the northwest corner of Connecticut. Once again, I found myself having to be at work at 5:30 a.m. and I loved it! I was given the position of supervisor of the breakfast and lunch shifts at the resort's restaurant. We served a buffet breakfast and the joint was really jumping, seven days a week.

Lime Rock, which is a renowned auto raceway, was near the Inn and many celebrities stayed with us, one of whom had very memorable blue eyes! When he appeared at the door for breakfast one day, I hurried him in to the lounge which was not being used that morning. I told him that my wait staff would not give him a moment's peace if he went into the regular dining room. I asked that I be given the privilege of serving him myself. He gratefully agreed and we had a very nice chat while he munched his toast and drank his coffee. Nice guy! (Sorry–no name dropping but I'm sure you can take a good guess!)

I loved being 'on the door' during the lunchtime hours. I assigned the customers to the wait staff and made sure that everything was going smoothly. I got to know our patrons very well, some of whom would only come to the Inn when they knew I was on duty. I always made sure that their favorite table was ready for them when they appeared at the door. I knew their favorite cocktails and often would bring their drinks to their table myself. If a patron was unhappy, it was my responsibility to smooth the troubled waters. If the dish room got backed up, I quickly cleared the servers' trays in order to facilitate service. If the wait staff got behind, I would often serve a complimentary cocktail to the customers who were waiting to keep everyone happy. I soon became a jack of all trades and I loved it. The Inn was always so busy that I went home happily exhausted just about every day. Once again as I look back, I realize that since I was so physically active during this time period, I don't recall my condition causing me many difficulties. There's that hindsight again! If only I'd known .....

For a time at the Inn, I planned banquets, weddings, and conferences. Planning weddings was very challenging but also very fulfilling. To see a bride beaming with delight as everything went off exactly as she had planned was very gratifying.

However, I preferred to be 'in the trenches', working directly with customers. I soon became closing manager and my days were suddenly reversed. I was now coming home at 3:00 a.m. I was responsible for making sure that the Inn was secured and had to handle any problems that had come up during the evening and nighttime hours. Once again, I was totally enjoying my work. I felt happy and fulfilled.

However, I was nearly forty years old at this point and I didn't see any prospects in my future of anyone sweeping me off my feet. My father's admonition that I should get married so I'd be cared for in my later years, echoed in my head. In the hospitality field, if you don't work, you generally don't get paid. There was certainly nothing like a retirement plan. So I did a reality check and decided that, despite the fact that I was feeling very gratified with my work, I had to look toward my future. No one was going to be taking care of me in my old age except me. I remembered my comment to my high school buddies that I didn't think I was going to live past the age of thirty five. I suddenly realized that that was not going to happen. So I bid a sad farewell to the hospitality field and looked to a prestigious preparatory high school in the same town.

CHAPTER 11

My Life's Work

I interviewed at The Hotchkiss School, a very prestigious private preparatory high school in Lakeville, Connecticut. During my interview, I made it abundantly clear that my main purpose for wishing to work at the School was because of their very generous retirement plan. (They always capitalized the word 'School' at Hotchkiss and it's a hard habit to break.) Once you had put in a certain number of years of service combined with your age, the School would pay for your health insurance for the remainder of your life. I thought that was certainly a wonderful incentive. They also doubled every dollar that you put into your retirement fund. As event planner for the Interlaken Inn, I had planned many conferences for the wife of the person doing my interview at Hotchkiss. The so-called interview was really just a formality. We both knew that I had the job if I wanted it.

I worked for eighteen years at this School and enjoyed every minute of it. The challenges which my position presented to me were very fulfilling. I have never been interested in having children of my own–my two wonderful cats filled my home with love. They were always up to some kind of tomfoolery that kept me on my toes! And they were such wonderful company. We had many conversations about the state of affairs in the world and in my own life.

Because I did not have any maternal instincts, I was delighted and, yes, rather surprised, no—make that shocked, when I found that I loved working with the teenagers who attended this very elite school. I became a second mother to many of them. This was a boarding school and many of the 'preps' (ninth-graders) suffered from homesickness. I soon became their mom away from home. My desk was the first place where the students would go for information and so I had to know everything that was going on in the School. I also got to meet many celebrities and wealthy entrepreneurs who sent their children there. Oh, the names I could drop! I was on first-name basis with some of them. Those were exciting times!

My superb, if I do say so myself, organizational skills really came into play in my work. I was able to juggle many balls at one time and still come out on top. My boss once said that he never had to ask me where anything was filed in my filing cabinet because everything was so logical (*thank you, Spock!*). My father had instilled a very strong work ethic in me and that really came in handy. I was always busy and kept everything in tip-top shape. The more I was able to do, the more they relied on me. I developed a wonderful relationship with my bosses and co-workers and soon became an integral part of the School.

CHAPTER 12

First Serious Injury

The next pivotal event in my life occurred at the age of 43. I tripped in a mall over an uneven walkway that was in the process of being repaired. Once again, I fell flat on my face and skinned my knee–yes, that poor right knee yet again! Being embarrassed at my clumsiness, I quickly got to my feet and we left the mall. From this point on, every time I fell (and that was many, many times), I would always catch my right toe on an uneven surface. A pattern was developing but I wasn't able to see it. There's that hindsight again!

I had landed on my outstretched left arm and my shoulder became very tender. After several weeks, I found a mass on the back of my left arm. My shoulder had begun to slip in and out of the joint and it was extremely painful. After suffering for several weeks, I decided that I needed to do something about the situation.

So I took myself off to see an orthopedic surgeon. He told me that the mass had developed because of the fall. He also said that my shoulder was subluxating, or slipping out of joint, and that I required immediate surgery to correct the problem. In order to calm my fears about the surgery, I remember him telling me that *I can do this operation with one hand tied behind my back.* I guess that bravado should have been a warning sign to me but it wasn't. I really liked that surgeon and I still do despite all that happened afterward.

So in March of 1992, I underwent surgery on my left shoulder. Unfortunately, the surgery resulted in severe damage to the axillary nerve. As a result, I have a permanent disability. I am unable to raise my left arm above shoulder level and it is weaker than my right arm. The triceps muscle is completely atrophied and my arm is badly deformed. It continues to be very painful to this day, some quarter century later.

Soldier on .....

Barbara and I decided to go to the Dutchess (New York) County Fair one balmy evening. B.J. Thomas was headlining and Barbara always liked him. So I thought I'd be game and go along. I had a sling on my left arm because of the shoulder injury. I had to wear a sling for many years in order to relieve some of the intense pain and also to let people know that they shouldn't jostle that arm. The pain would be excruciating if anyone bumped into me. I was wearing a bright pink baseball cap that evening. I guess between that cap and my sling, B.J. somehow picked me out of the crowd. He motioned for me to come down to the stage but I was sure that he wasn't gesturing to me. So I ignored his invitation and continued to enjoy the show. Barbara asked me later why I hadn't gone down to the stage. *Do you really think he was gesturing to me?!* *Yes!* Barbara said. Since I really didn't know him at the time, I wasn't terribly upset over the missed opportunity. But now that I've really come to know his music and what a nice person he is, I am so bummed that I didn't get to meet him! After all, anyone who travels with his cat must be an incredibly caring person! *Hey, B.J., if you're reading this, do you remember me? You put on a wonderful concert and I'm so very sorry that I didn't get to meet you! What a fool I was!!*

I had additional surgery performed by an extremely talented neurosurgeon in December of 1992 to try to repair the nerve damage that had occurred during the initial surgery on my shoulder. However, the neurosurgeon who performed that surgery told me that the nerve was 'toast' and that nothing could be done to correct the damage. *You'll have to learn to live with it,* he advised me. *Yes,* I thought to myself, *I know very well how to live with problems. It's second nature to me after all these years so why not just add another one to the list?*

My right knee was so painful at this point that I was only able to hobble around very slowly. I was constantly at the orthopedic surgeon's office for aspiration of fluid off my knee. I refused to use a cane, however, because that would have been giving in to my difficulties.

I started doing physical therapy, which was extremely painful, supposedly for my disabled left arm. My physical therapist felt rather challenged by my physical difficulties. She gave me numerous exercises to try to correct the problems with my shoulder and knee but to no avail. She became rather puzzled and very appalled over my lack of core strength. I was unable to stand on one foot for more than two seconds without toppling over. If she asked me to try it with my eyes closed, I wasn't able to stand on one foot for even one second. I was totally unable to do even one sit up. I couldn't figure out how I had become so totally out of shape!

Once again, I thought of myself as just being incredibly weak. Since I was now sitting at a desk for eight hours or more a day, I think that contributed to my problem becoming so acute. I always felt that my problem was my fault and that if I were a stronger person, I would be able to somehow overcome it. Even though I was very faithful in my physical therapy exercises, nothing would help my poor balance. *You have to try harder,* the therapist would admonish me. *I am trying harder. I'm doing my very best. Nothing helps,* I declared to her.

Echoes of that first country doctor's offhanded comment filled my ears once again as it did many times over the course of my lifetime. *There's nothing wrong with you.* I added to my own misery when I told myself that I was just incredibly clumsy and weak.

Oh, well, I thought. *I guess this is the way I am and always will be. Nothing will ever help me.* It took another fifteen years of suffering before someone actually listened to me and helped discover the cause of my problem. In the meantime,…..

Soldier on …..

CHAPTER 13

My Guardian Angel

At this point in my life, it was becoming more and more difficult to hide whatever my problem was. I did my best, however, to just keep going on as if everything was normal. As if I was normal! But I knew deep down in my heart that that just was not true. Most people were not even aware of the magnitude of my difficulties, I hid them so well but every day was such a struggle for me. I wanted so much to feel normal and to be able to do everything everyone else could do so easily.

The one person from whom I did not hide my issue was my wonderful sister, Barbara. She was well aware of what I was going through and did her best to help me cope with it. She would always offer me her arm if the surface underfoot was uneven. She would drive me to the door of the mall if I felt I couldn't walk that far because of my painful knee. She watched over me carefully, trying to protect me from falls. I began calling her 'My Guardian Angel' and I continue to do so to this very day. If it weren't for her, I'm not sure what would have happened to me. But I hid the steadily increasing magnitude of my problem from her as well. I didn't want to worry her; I was worried enough for the both of us.

At this point, I was no longer wearing a sling for my painful arm. However, the fact that my shoulder muscles were so badly atrophied caused my deplorable balance issues to become even worse (at least, that's what I blamed it on). I couldn't come up with any other reason for my constant trips and tumbles.

Despite Barbara's best efforts to keep me on my feet, however, I continued to suffer numerous falls. It was not unusual for me to stumble or even fall several times during the week. As a result, my right knee was now severely damaged. I remember one day when I was working in the office at School that I tried to get up to go to the ladies' room. Because of my serious urinary frequency, I had to make this trip numerous times throughout the day. I found that I suddenly could not put any weight on my right leg! I quickly sat right back down again and called the School's infirmary and a nurse was kind enough to bring me a cane. From that point on, my cane became part of my everyday wardrobe. I had to give in to the fact that I could no longer walk without it.

Once again, Barbara drove me down to the emergency room that day where I was advised to have further surgery on my knee. I was only in my early fifties at this point and I was now forced to rely on a cane to get around. Even though I continued to go to physical therapy, my knee caused me severe pain. I continued to have my knee aspirated frequently and large amounts of fluid were removed every time. That helped ease the pain for a brief period of time but it never lasted. Within a few days, the pain and swelling in my knee would be just as intense as it had been before the aspiration.

I continued to hobble around, finding it so painful to even get from my bed to the bathroom without the aid of a cane. Because I was forced to move so slowly, I frequently did not make it to the bathroom on time. I also realized that many times I would not feel any urge to urinate but then suddenly, I would be overcome with a sudden and absolute urgency. Many times when this happened, I was totally unable to control the flow of urine. Ashamed, I would feel the hot liquid flow down my legs and I was unable to do anything to stop it. Squeezing as hard as I could had no effect whatsoever. It was as if the urine had a mind of its own. I always hid an extra pair of underwear in my desk and in my purse, just in case I had another one of my frequent accidents. I started buying *Depends* in large quantities. These were certainly not good times .....

Soldier on .....

Finally, in 2005, I agreed to yet another surgery on my right knee. The orthopedic surgeon wanted to 'scrape' the back of my knee to see if that would help my situation. I blithely hoped that maybe this procedure would finally help alleviate some of the pain and increase my mobility (it didn't!). I thought that at this point, I didn't really have very much to lose! I was becoming rather desperate to be free of such intense pain and limited mobility. I HATED feeling so helpless and having to rely on those around me to do things that I should be able to do for myself.

I never seemed to do well with scheduling all of my many tests, surgeries, and physical therapy sessions. I always wound up going someplace far away in the dead of winter! (I live in the Northeast and snow and ice were always an issue.)

Well, that was the case yet again. The day before surgery, a severe ice storm was predicted but I was determined to have this new surgery performed on my knee. I was in so much pain and could not put any weight on my right leg. Selfishly, I insisted that Barbara drive me to the medical center which was two hours away from home.

I was scheduled for the first case in the morning (7:00 a.m.) but emergency after emergency came in. I guess all that ice was causing a lot of accidents and some pretty banged up people. I had not been allowed to eat since midnight and here we were coming on to the afternoon. After a while, I was no longer interested in eating but my thirst was overwhelming! I wasn't even allowed a sip of water. Without the nurse's knowledge, I finally swished some water in my mouth and settled down to continue to wait ..... and wait ..... and wait .....

Barbara nervously kept looking out the window in the medical center and watched as ice began coating the tree branches. I was finally in the operating room at 5:00 p.m. and was discharged at about 10:00 p.m. The roads were covered in ice and the driving was very treacherous. The only fools out on the roads were emergency vehicles and the two of us! I suggested that we pull into a motel for the night but Barbara said she'd be more comfortable taking care of me in her own home. So we drove for miles and miles through ice and snow at ten miles per hour. I really didn't mind—I was still a little loopy from the anesthesia! But the knuckles on Barbara's hands were white as she gripped the steering wheel and tried to keep us from sliding off the road and into a ditch!

As I look back on my life, it's quite obvious that I suffered tremendous physical pain and mental anguish. However, I feel so guilty about all the anxiety and stress that I caused my sister over the years. She was saddled with watching over me, scraping me off the sidewalk when I fell yet again, and taking me to all of my innumerable medical appointments. I think she suffered as much, if not more, than I did. I will be forever grateful to her for all of her love and devotion. There's just no way one can ever repay a debt like that. I am so blessed that my sister was always there for me. I know that she will receive her just reward, over and above anything I could ever hope to give her, when she strolls through those Pearly Gates that are opened wide and Jesus smiles at her as He says, "Come on in. We've been waiting for you."

CHAPTER 14

The Challenges

It was fortunate that I was now sitting at a desk rather than running around at the Inn. With my physical impairments, I would never have been able to continue doing such a physically demanding job. My right knee was in no better shape than it had been before this most recent surgery. I continued to rely on a cane to get around. My left shoulder was still badly damaged from the surgery in 1992. I was rather disabled but I continued to get through each day as best I could. I tried very hard not to show the agony that I was in but my co-workers could read it in my face.

Despite my disabilities, my supervisors and co-workers at The Hotchkiss School embraced me and were very supportive. They helped me whenever I found that I was having some difficulty performing my job duties due to my physical limitations. Although I had not returned to using my sling to help alleviate some of the pain I felt in my shoulder, something as simple as straightening out a pile of papers proved to be challenging for me. No one at School ever once suggested that I leave my position due to my problems. My bosses frequently told me that they wanted me there for my brain, not my shoulder or my knee! And the students really looked up to me so that helped a lot.

My urinary frequency and incontinence became more and more of a problem at this time. My 'accidents' were occurring more frequently. It had gotten to the point where I now kept several changes of underwear, panty hose, and a hefty supply of *Depends* in my desk drawer for those days when I had an accident. Unfortunately, that was pretty often, sometimes as much as twice a day. Working with kids, I was always afraid that they'd discover my secret. But if anyone noticed, no one said anything. I had hoped that my problem was not evident to them or to my co-workers. I was blissful in my ignorance.

The house I lived in had a very long driveway. If my knee wasn't hurting too badly, I would hobble up and down the driveway just for a little exercise. It never failed that as soon as I went back into the house, I would lose total control of my urine. I would have to clean up and change underwear again before heading off to work. No matter how hard I tried, I just could not maintain control of my urine. How humiliating!

I also noticed that ten minutes after I got into bed, I would have to get up to void. I tried very hard not to give in to these urges but I thought that if I didn't, I might lose control of my urine while I was asleep. As a result, I would have to get up four or five times every night to urinate. I started doing Kegel exercises with a vengeance but they didn't help my situation at all. I'd later learn that my incontinence had nothing to do with my bladder and everything to do with my brain.

CHAPTER 15

There's That Look Again!

I had a tremendous amount of respect for my ophthalmologist. He had incredible abilities and he kept abreast of all of the latest research. He was very thorough in his care of my vision and my family's vision. As a matter of fact, he was able to save some of my father's eyesight when a previous eye doctor had failed to diagnose glaucoma.

He very patiently worked with me as I struggled to adjust to contact lenses. I was able to tolerate them for a while but eventually gave up on them. Putting pieces of plastic in my eyeballs made me shiver! He always made sure to do every test possible to ensure that I would not lose my vision to glaucoma as my father almost had. I am extremely near-sighted and finding the right prescription for glasses proved to be a challenge. I hated to have to wear thick Coke lenses and so he found a lab that could make my lenses thinner in frames that were a bit more stylish. Well, if you consider 'granny' glasses stylish! But they were very 'in' at the time.

Since I had very deliberately decided never to tell anyone of my 'weird' symptoms, I don't know whatever came over me one day while I was in my eye doctor's office. It was during a lull in his testing that I thought I'd make a confession to him. I remember telling him that there were times when my head felt as if it were swelling so much that the bows of my eyeglasses actually made indentations on my temples. Well now, here it comes again! That look of disbelief and skepticism filled his expression. What else did I expect?! He had known me for many years and I guess he didn't think I was prone to exaggeration but really ..... Like that country doctor of my childhood, he just looked askance at me. I don't think he even made any comment at all. We continued on with the examination and swept my statement under the rug. I was sorry that I had even brought it up. I was afraid that he'd think I was some kind of a lunatic.

It was the same thing whenever I tried to tell anyone of my problems. Believe me, I never confessed anything like that to anyone again for many, many years. Sometimes it takes a two by four up the side of the head to make me see the light! And thankfully, God would later provide that 'enlightenment' but that was still some years in the future.

An interesting note: After I had had my brain surgery (more on that later!), my sister happened to be in my ophthalmologist's office. She told him about my condition and his eyebrows went up into his hairline–gee, just like Spock! Now, who had a look of disbelief and embarrassment?!

In the meantime,

Soldier on .....

CHAPTER 16

Why Can't I Get Up!?

I was at my sister Barbara's house one cold winter's day. We were trying to shovel the snow off her deck. Due to constant physical therapy and exercises, the pain level in my knee was now at a more tolerable level. Barbara was always helping me so I thought I'd try to help her for once. Well, of course, staying on my feet was never an option for me. I slipped on the ice and went down once again in a crumpled heap. Okay, so I couldn't blame this fall on my 'condition', whatever that was. My 'weird' problem made its presence known again when I tried to get up under my own power and found that I absolutely could not get up off that blasted deck!

Once again, Barbara came to my rescue–or she tried to, anyway. She pulled and lugged on me as I struggled to gain my feet. Despite our best efforts, I simply could not stand up! The ice wasn't the problem as I had slid on my rump to an area that was clear of snow and ice. The issue was that my legs just would not lift me up, no matter how much I struggled! This was the first time that I had ever experienced this total lack of control over my legs. Every time in the past when I had fallen, I had been able to scramble to my feet, usually terribly embarrassed at my incredible clumsiness, but not this time!

So, here I was sitting in a crumpled heap, totally powerless to achieve a standing position. After what seemed like an eternity of pulling on me while I willed my legs to cooperate, Barbara finally said that we'd have to call the fire department to get me on my feet! I was mortified! I knew several of the guys in the fire department and I didn't want anyone to see me sitting on my posterior in a pile of snow. They would want to know why I couldn't get up. But here I was, unable to stand up. How embarrassing–no, make that *humiliating!*

I was only fifty five years old and that television commercial played in my mind: *'I've fallen and I can't get up!'* I had often scoffed at that commercial and had said how ridiculous it was that someone couldn't get off the floor. Now, however, I painfully realized that it was happening to me. *What is going on with me?* I wondered. *Why can't I get up? This is absolutely ridiculous!* Suddenly, strength came to me and I was able to get up on my own. I clambered to my feet much to the relief of both of us. I quickly made my way into the house to warm up after sitting out in the cold for so long. Poor Barbara had to finish shoveling the deck by herself. I surely was not going to risk landing on my derrière again. After making sure that I wasn't hurt, I drove the short distance to my home, tail between my legs. I was totally disgusted and felt absolutely degraded by my clumsiness and weakness.

I am such a poor excuse for a Human being, I admonished myself. *I must do something to try to get stronger but what? Nothing ever helps.* I was sure that things couldn't get any worse than this. Little did I know just how bad things would soon become. This was just the very tip of the iceberg. If I had had a crystal ball at that time that had shown me just how badly my life would soon deteriorate, I probably would have drawn myself into a fetal position and just given up on life. But I didn't know the meaning of 'giving up' so once again, I listened to my mantra .....

Soldier on .....

CHAPTER 17

The Cape

There was one time when I decided to take my mother to Cape Cod for the weekend. The Cape was about five hours from where she lived. Although I drove short distances, I was not comfortable driving for any length of time due to my symptoms. I was afraid that if I had one of those 'white outs' while I was behind the wheel that I could hurt or even kill someone. I didn't care about myself–because of my issues, frankly, I really didn't care whether I lived or died. I only drove locally and did that with a tremendous amount of care. So that meant that Barbara would always do any long-distance driving. Whatever possessed me to undertake this trip to the Cape remains a mystery to both my sister and me to this day!

Anyway, Mom and I had a very nice visit to the seashore and enjoyed some really delicious seafood. We both adored shrimp and lobster and this was a seafood lover's paradise! If we had had the necessary capital, my mother and I would both no doubt be living by the ocean. I always felt so alive when I had my toes in the surf. Listening to the cries of the gulls as they dove below the surface of the water in search of their dinner always had such a calming effect on me.

I was amazed that I had not fallen flat on my face throughout the entire weekend. I should have known better! As we were leaving the Cape, I stopped at a gift shop where I had seen something I wanted to bring back for Barbara. I walked to the front door on a sidewalk that was constructed of wooden boards made to resemble the deck of a pirate's ship–or in my case, the plank!

Well, if there was an uneven surface anywhere, I would surely find it! The toe of my right foot (always my right foot!) caught on an uneven board and there I went yet again! I fell flat out on my stomach, my head filling up with cotton as usual. That miserable feeling of nausea struck with a vengeance. I had to lie there for a few seconds before I was able to logroll onto my back. By the time I scraped myself up off the sidewalk, my left ankle was throbbing and already swelling. My poor right knee was also throbbing and bloody as well. We had already checked out of our motel and so we had to get home. I crawled into the driver's seat and put on a brave face for my mother. I assured her (okay, so I blatantly lied to my mother!) that I was just fine but she knew better.

We stopped for gas and the gas attendant (those were the days when they actually pumped your gas for you!) saw my bloody and torn-up left hand. "Your hand is all bloody!" he exclaimed. "Are you going to get it looked at? I can give you directions to the hospital." This was from a boy who was maybe seventeen years old. Pretty caring for such a young person, wouldn't you say? I hoped I thanked him properly for his concern. *Nah,* I said, *it's just a little scrape!* (Didn't those brave cowboys in Westerns always say, 'It's only a flesh wound'?)

Soldier on .....

The trip back from Cape Cod was pretty harrowing. My left ankle continued to swell as it throbbed very badly. Since I drove a standard shift, I had to use my left foot, despite the pain. At one point, my left foot had actually gone numb and I had to pray that my foot on the clutch was doing what my mind was willing it to do. (Perhaps I should mention here that my mother had never learned how to drive although she was pretty good at slamming on the brakes from the passenger seat!) So getting us back safely to Connecticut was solely on my shoulders. I didn't have much of a choice as we were travelling along the Massachusetts Turnpike. Because I was always afraid to admit to my limitations, it never would have occurred to me to tell my mother the truth. I thought, *I can do this. I've gotten us this far and I can get us safely home. Please dear God, help me. I don't want my mother to get hurt because of me.*

Well, I probably would have been all right if the weather had been bright and sunny. But, of course, that wasn't how my luck ran. Even though it was only late October, it started to snow and sleet began pelting the windshield while we were on the turnpike. Our relaxing weekend at the Cape was now overshadowed by nerve-wracking anxiety. All of the good times we had had were soon forgotten as we slipped and slid along the highway.

My mother was scared to death that we'd find ourselves in a pile up on the side of the road. I have to admit that my knuckles were pretty white on the steering wheel that day. After taking several more hours than it should have taken if the roads had been clear, we finally neared home. I was never so happy to see our exit and safe haven at the end of the highway. Needless to say, I never attempted any long trips like that ever again. I had learned my lesson the hard way. I had to accept that fact that I just was not capable of driving long distances because of my problem, whatever it was. And I would never again put anyone in danger because of my mysterious problem.

CHAPTER 18

Things Really Start Going Downhill

My life continued to be a struggle each and every day. Without warning, my legs would become weak and I would suffer from sudden and unexplained falls. I suffered from dizzy spells and would feel as if the ship rocked–a sudden momentary attack of vertigo. During these episodes, I would become extremely nauseated and my head always felt as if it was going to explode. I was walking across a large room one time during one of these attacks of vertigo. If a chair had not been nearby, I would have gone flat out on the floor.

My gait was so unsteady that many times I probably appeared to be inebriated. I often worried that I would be stopped by a police officer for some minor traffic violation. I lived in fear that I would be told to walk the center line. I knew I was not able to do that without stumbling even though I was stone cold sober.

As I said before, I lived alone in a small house near my place of employment. I had developed a great fondness for gardening, thanks to my sister, Barbara. Her gardens were incredibly extensive and very beautiful. She taught me so much about flowers and how to cultivate them.

Because my knee was in such bad shape, I was unable to kneel when I did gardening. I had a little seat with wheels that I would use while tending my flowers. One evening, when I got home from work, I noticed that there were some weeds by my lamp post. Since it was getting late, I didn't bother getting out my trusty little seat. Rather, I sat down on the low stone wall that lined my driveway. Once I had finished pulling the weeds, I tried to stand up. No such luck! I could not, for the life of me, get to my feet! My legs just would not lift me to a standing position!

Since I lived alone, I thought, *Well now, isn't this is just great?! It's getting dark and no one even knows that I'm out here!* My closest (actually, my only) neighbors' home was very far away from my house and so they wouldn't hear me even if I shouted at the top of my lungs. *What in the world am I going to do?!* I struggled and struggled to stand up but to no avail. I finally had to inch my way on my rear end up the wall as it gradually sloped upward. I finally got to the highest point on the wall. I went down on my knees and then lifted my rear end up in the air. I was surely glad at that point that I didn't have any neighbors to witness such an ungraceful act but I didn't care! At least I was finally able to stand up! Hallelujah! It's amazing how you begin to see little victories when you're mired in whatever was my condition.

Shaking my head at what I thought, once again, was my own incredible weakness, I was finally able to go inside the house. My two cats were not very happy that their dinner was so late. But when they saw how upset I was, they let me off the hook! I realized that if I had not been able to finally stand up, I would have spent the night on the cold and hard concrete. My only other option had been to crawl into the house on my hands and knees but that wouldn't have gotten me anywhere. I wouldn't have been able to put the key in the lock. Keep in mind that this was way before the advent of cell phones. I never told my sister of this terrifying event. It would have frightened her as much as it had terrified me.

What about the next time when something like this happens? What will I do? I shuddered with dread that whole night. *Things can't possibly get any worse than this, can they?* No, I thought. Nothing could be as bad as what had just happened that evening. Little did I know that the evening's incident was a cake walk compared to what I would be forced to face in the future.

Soldier on .....

CHAPTER 19

I Must Retire Before……..

Okay, I'm getting pretty depressed here reliving all these dismal memories. As I was writing my story, I found that I had to take frequent breaks to dispel the distressing recollections. When I think back to how bleak my life was, I absolutely shudder with despair. Are you feeling despondent too just reading this tale of woe? Oh, but don't worry….. there's a very bright light at the end of this dark and dreary tunnel.

I was held in very high esteem at my place of employment. I was loyal, hard-working, and highly dependable. However, after eighteen years of service there, I was finding it more and more difficult to concentrate and I could barely walk because of increasing knee pain. Although I was always successful in completing my duties, I was finding it harder and harder to do just that. Everything was becoming more and more of a challenge. What had once been easy to do was now an arduous task. It seemed as though the ability to even think was beginning to elude me.

As I neared my fifty fifth birthday, I realized that I was beginning to have tremendous difficulty concentrating. Putting a thought together in my head and then being able to express it was becoming almost impossible. There were times when my boss would be speaking to me and it was as if he was speaking in Greek. I just couldn't understand what he was saying for a moment. He used to tease me by saying that I was 'asleep at the switch'. Then, the vagueness would clear and I was back in the moment. Oh, how I hated when that happened. It made me feel so stupid and inept.

As I said previously, one of the main reasons that I went to work at this wonderful School was their fabulous retirement program. After a certain length of service, the School would pay for my health insurance for the rest of my life. That was a pretty big incentive to work there. But over and above all that and the other benefits they offered, it was just simply a fabulous place to work. They really cared about their employees. We were like one big happy family. Everyone looked out for one another and our supervisors were more like friends than our bosses. Indeed, I attended many dinners and parties at my bosses' homes.

When I first came back to work after having had the original ill-fated surgery on my shoulder, my boss asked me to type a letter for him. I panicked a bit and jokingly said that it might take me all day to type it since I could only use one hand! He very kindly said, "Then, let it take all day. I'm in no hurry. Just do the best you can like you always do." See, how our words can have such a lasting impression on us?

As I neared eighteen years of employment, I began to think that I was beginning to fail in the performance of my duties. I didn't want the School to look badly upon me even though they had always been so supportive of me. Doing my work satisfactorily (to MY high standards) was becoming more and more difficult to accomplish. Since I was now eligible to receive retirement benefits from the School at this point, I decided that I had better leave my position before I was no longer able to perform my functions at all. So, I sadly gave my notice and bid farewell to my friends and co-workers in June of 2006.

CHAPTER 20

We Move to Massachusetts!

My sister and I each owned a home in the same town in Connecticut. We decided to join forces and move somewhere together after we both retired. We drove all throughout the Northeast, trying to decide on an area where we'd like to live. We were driving back from Vermont one weekend, totally discouraged. Every area we looked at seemed to be depressed and rundown. We were absolutely exhausted when we saw a sign for Northampton, MA. After having driven for hours through these one-horse towns, we came upon the main street of Northampton. It looked like New York City with its bright lights and welcoming feel. We checked into the rather elegant Hotel Northampton and enjoyed our stay immensely. Even though it was very painful for me to do any walking, we managed to stroll down the busy streets with all the wonderful boutiques.

We looked at each other and smiled as we agreed that we liked this area. We signed on with a real estate agency in Easthampton, MA. Our real estate agent was very patient in showing us numerous houses around the region. I remember one house she showed us that was built on the side of a hill. I looked in horror at the hill surrounding the property. "I can't live here," I exclaimed. When we were leaving, we went down the front walkway which was on a very steep slope. There was no handrail on the steps so Barbara had to walk down the stairs backward while bracing me as I very carefully made my way down to level ground. I breathed a sigh of relief that I hadn't tumbled down those wicked-looking steps and hurried to the safety of the car. Our agent later asked Barbara, "What's wrong with Jeanne?" Barbara brushed off the concern, saying that I simply had a fear of heights.

It took us a while but we finally found a beautiful home in a small town near Northampton, Massachusetts. My sister had already resigned her position at the nursing home where she had worked for twenty three years.

She continued to negotiate the sale of the house that we thought was 'the one'. I was still working at the time that we actually bought the house. I had only seen pictures of it on-line and saw it for the first time in person on the day of the closing.

Although the house was beautiful and in excellent condition, I was horrified to see that there were four half-levels. In order to get upstairs to my bedroom, I had to climb a half-flight of stairs. My knee was so painful that I was finding that I literally had to pull myself up on the banister to get up those blasted stairs.

There was no bathroom, not even a powder room, on the main level and so again, I had to climb those stairs every time I had to use the bathroom. Keep in mind that I was suffering from severe urinary frequency and more frequent incontinence so that meant that I had to climb those steps pretty frequently. I tried to plan my trips to limit the amount of times I had to journey upstairs.

I was so envious of Barbara as she flew up and down those same stairs. It seemed that nothing ever stopped her, thank heavens! I needed her to be my legs for me. She would frequently get something I needed from upstairs. At times, I felt so guilty because it seemed as if she was acting as my servant. But Barbara has always been a cheerful, caring, and kind person. She was placed on this earth to do for others. Since she was a certified nursing assistant, she cared for both our parents in their home until their deaths. She never once complained, either about having to care for them or having to watch over and care for her baby sister. What a blessing she was and still is.

I did my best to continue just getting through each and every day. Our property was built on a slope and I found that I was terrified that I would lose my balance and tumble down the hill. I developed a terrible fear of falling. I knew that if I fell, I would do serious damage to myself and that I would simply shatter into a million pieces. I seemed to have developed a fear of everything. I became socially withdrawn and hated when I heard the doorbell ring.

Soldier on .....

Because I felt that my problems all stemmed from my own weakness, I was even more determined than ever to try to do my share of the work. We had four acres of extensive gardens and lawn. Needless to say, there was a lot of work to do to maintain it in the splendid manner that the builder and previous owner had kept it. I would always try to find some project that I could do while sitting down. I painted, weeded, and trimmed grass all while sitting on my little rolling seat. I did anything that I felt safe doing.

Barbara mowed the four acres of grass on a riding mower. However, there was a slope along the road that had to be hand mowed. Even though I was very unsteady on my feet, it seemed unfair that Barbara should have to do that mowing as well. So, I tried very valiantly to hand mow that blasted front slope. I did it for two summers and then felt so afraid that I was going to fall that we finally hired someone to mow it. Interesting to note that after my surgery (more on that later), that slope was no longer so steep and scary. I was able to mow it without any problem whatsoever.

Not only was I determined to do my share of the outside work, I also insisted on doing a big part of the housework. Barbara was working part-time and so I was left with most of the work inside. One time when I decided to clean my shower stall, I put a stool in the shower so I could scrub the bottom of the glass enclosure. Bending over usually sent me into a swoon! So here I was, soaking wet, sitting in the shower and I tried to get up. *Oh, no*, I thought. *I can't get up!* My legs just would not support me! *Why am I so blasted weak? How could this be happening again?!* So there I sat, soaking wet, for two hours until Barbara finally came home from work. I yelled down the stairs, "Can you help me get up?" Once again, my thoughts of being weak and helpless crashed down on me. How humiliating! Would this misery ever end?

CHAPTER 21

From Bad to Worse

Concentrating on anything became extremely difficult. To my horror, I found that I could no longer balance my checkbook. I still had an account in my previous bank and wrote checks on that balance. Unfortunately, my money was actually in my new account. I was shocked when I received overdraft notices! *How could that be??!! I have the money to cover these checks!* Then I realized what I had done. My accounts were so badly messed up that it almost required a CPA to figure it out. I remember saying to Barbara that I was feeling so overwhelmed and unable to cope. In fact, I didn't even want to continue trying to cope. It had become so difficult to just get through the trials I faced each day. Okay, I'm really getting depressed here again ..... All these miserable memories are so painful.

There were times when I would try to start walking and my feet would feel as if they were glued to the floor. I began walking very slowly and carefully and prayed every solitary day that I wouldn't fall AGAIN! Despite the fact that I was only 57 years old at this time, my gait had become increasingly shuffling, much like a person with Parkinson's disease. My unsteadiness and lack of balance became unbearable.

I had to use the handicapped stall when using the rest room. I needed to hold on to the safety rail to maintain my balance. My severe urinary urgency and incontinence were now accompanied by occasional stool incontinence. Imagine my horror when I had to clean my own feces out of the white wall-to-wall carpeting in our house. It was bad enough when my cats missed their litter box and now here I was adding to the misery! Once again, I was absolutely humiliated.

I found that I was unable to get up from the bed or a chair without using my hands to push myself up. Again, I thought that I was just incredibly weak. When I tried to get up from the couch, I would struggle and struggle, falling back into a seated position over and over again before I finally managed to stand up. Barbara, my cheering squad, would say, *Come on, you can do it! Keep trying!* I thought, *How embarrassing to be so feeble and nearly helpless. How did my life become so out of control??!! How can I be so damned weak??!!*

I remember that I once almost tipped over a small bistro table in a restaurant because the chair had no arms on which to push myself up. I caught the table just before it was going to topple over. It took several attempts and my sister's helping arm to finally get me to stand up. Oh, how ashamed I felt! I thought that things could not possibly get any worse. How wrong I was! Each time I foolishly thought that, future events would soon prove just how much worse things could really get.

One day going up the very steep steps at church, I caught my right toe yet again and sprawled all over the stone steps. A parishioner stopped and stood by me. I was no longer embarrassed anymore when I fell–after all, I had had plenty of practice. I asked the gentleman to please just go around me. He kindly said that he was waiting for me to gather myself so he could help me up. Now, there's a true

Christian. *Thank you, sir! God bless you!* When we got into the church, I discovered that my poor right knee was bloody yet again! And yes, it was throbbing quite nicely, thank you very much.

Soldier on .....

A few weeks later, I was carrying bags of groceries up the steps at home. As to be expected at this point, my right toe caught the step and I tripped once again. I fell flat out, scraping the side of my face on the hard stone step while my glasses flew off my face. And, of course, that beleaguered right knee was scraped to bits once again.

I began crying and screamed, *What is wrong with me? Normal people don't just fall like I do! I must have Parkinson's disease or multiple sclerosis!! This can't be normal!* Once again, Barbara was there for me and assured me that my symptoms didn't fit either of those diagnoses. I was placated for the moment but I was finding it harder and harder to .....

Soldier on .....

At this point, I knew for certain that I would be doomed to spend the rest of my life confined to a wheelchair. In truth, I thought that at least if I was in a wheelchair, I wouldn't have to worry about falling anymore. I knew the crushing weight of total despair at that point. *I felt like I was a hundred years old. Why won't God take me and put an end to this misery? I don't want to live like this anymore. Life is just not worth living. I'm not contributing anything to anyone. I'm just a drain on Barbara and society in general. I don't have the right to use up the oxygen on this planet .....*

Things were really starting to reach a critical point. I didn't know how much longer I could go on like this. As a matter of fact, at the end of each day, I was so grateful that I was one day closer to the end of it all. I was so looking forward to the blessing of death and being in heaven, no longer burdened by this debilitating problem.

I guess the most traumatic event after our move to Massachusetts was when my legs simply gave out from under me one night. I crumpled to the floor and Barbara yelled up the stairs, *What was that crash?* Embarrassed yet again by my clumsiness and total weakness, I lied and said that I had just dropped a book. I struggled and struggled, became incontinent, and once again, started to cry. I hated it when I cried. It showed how weak and helpless I was. *How did I get to be so helpless, so decrepit, so unworthy of taking up space?!*

No matter how hard I tried, I simply could not stand up! Since I was not able to get up off the floor on my own, I had no choice but to call Barbara. Once again, my Guardian Angel lugged and pulled on me with no luck. She tried putting a footstool under me to help me get at least a few inches off the floor. I was mortified yet again when I crashed onto the stool and shattered its legs. I had never felt such total degradation .....

Finally, Barbara said that we'd have to call the fire department to get me off the floor. Our wonderful neighbor was the fire chief and we knew he'd be over to our house in a flash. But I had been able to keep my secret from our neighbors and so I didn't want to call him. Besides, it was very late at night.

After about fifteen minutes on the floor, I gritted my teeth, said that this was ridiculous, struggled to my knees, and fell face down on the bed. I went to sleep that night, soaked with urine. But I certainly wasn't about to risk the possibility that I would fall again so I didn't want to wash at that point. Also, I didn't think Barbara's back could withstand another episode like the one that we had both just endured. This was

the lowest point of my life. I felt that I had just experienced
the depths of hell. All I wanted to do was just crawl into bed
and stay there for the rest of my life, curled into a fetal ball of
worthless flesh. I wanted to see my journey and my life come
to a crashing end. It just wasn't worth living anymore …..

CHAPTER 22

My Faith in God

My faith continued to be a very important part of my life. I found a prayer to the Virgin Mary that was to be said whenever you had a fear of falling:

Take my hand, oh Blessed Mother.
Hold me firmly, lest I fall.
I grow nervous while walking
and humbly on thee call.
Guide me over every crossing.
Watch me when I'm on the stairs.
Let me know that you're beside me.
Listen to my fervent prayer.

Bring me to my destination,
safely along the way.
Bless my every undertaking
and my duties for the day.

And when evening creeps upon me,
I'll never fear to be alone.
Once again, oh, Blessed Mother,
Take my hand and lead me home.

I began saying that prayer numerous times every day especially when I went outdoors. I knew there were many traps and snares lurking out there, just waiting to trip me up. I always felt protected whenever I said that prayer. I continued to walk very slowly and carefully and prayed every day that I wouldn't fall–**AGAIN.**

It was at this point that I started to pray that God would let me die so I wouldn't have to suffer any longer. My life was nothing but misery. I felt that I was just barely existing and that my life served no purpose whatsoever. As I said before, I felt that I had become a drain on society and certainly a tremendous burden to my sister.

Although thoughts of suicide began to plague me, being a devout Catholic, I would never have attempted to take my own life as a way to end my torment. I could not have done that to my family. But I have to admit that I was becoming very envious of anyone who died. Their struggles in this life were over and yet mine went on and on and on ......

I continued to find everyday life so much of a challenge. I tried to do whatever I could to help around the house and grounds. With almost four acres of gardens, there certainly was plenty to do. I chose what I would do based on my abilities ..... or should I say, disabilities. If I was able to sit down while doing something, then that was what I tried to do. My sister was sixty five years old at this point and had to do the bulk of the heavy work. My guilt level soared but I was doing the best that I could. She never once complained, being the Guardian Angel that she is. *Just do what you can,* she'd say. *I'll do the rest.* I thought, *God bless you, Barbara. You surely have earned your place in heaven with the rest of the angels.*

'Soldier on' was no longer an option for me. I had given up on trying to be brave and no longer tried to ignore my problems. I cried myself to sleep many nights, just begging God to take me. I knew that in heaven I would no longer have to endure this agony. I felt that I had already served my penance here on Earth and that I would surely take the express elevator right up to heaven. Maybe it was because I had hit rock bottom that God finally took pity on me. During this time, I kept telling my sister that I felt that God was trying to tell me something but I just wasn't getting it. It took a two by four up the side of my head to finally get His message.

CHAPTER 23

Someone Finally Listened!

God does work in mysterious and wonderful ways. It was during the fall of 2006 when my sister insisted that we go to a local business fair. Being new to the area, she felt that it would be good to see what was available in our local town. Although I found it difficult and very painful to walk even with the help of a cane, we slowly made our way around the building and grounds.

The good Lord pointed me toward a booth where Dr. Henré Andosca of *Easthampton Chiropractic* was doing evaluations. Although I had had three surgeries, countless aspirations, and extensive physical therapy on my right knee, I was still in a great deal of pain and had very limited mobility, necessitating my continued dependence on a cane. Just walking from my bed to the bathroom, which was only a few feet away, caused me excruciating agony. I had to hold on to the walls and sink if I didn't have my cane handy.

My father frequently had to see a chiropractor for an 'adjustment' of his spine. He always said that once you start to see a chiropractor, you will always be forced to rely on one. He warned me not to get drawn into that trap. With this admonition from my father in mind, I doubted that this chiropractor would be able to do anything to help me. Despite my hesitation, however, we decided to wait until he returned from lunch. To be truthful, I was just so glad that I was able to sit down while we waited for him! I firmly believe that it was God's hand that made us wait that day. That's the two by four I mentioned earlier! Looking back on it, I could almost hear God saying, *This girl needs some serious help. She's not figuring it out on her own. Let me point her in the right direction.*

While we were waiting, the chiropractor's assistant told us that she had suffered severe whiplash in a car accident. She told us of the tremendous amount of pain she had been in and how she had been unable to move her neck. She said that 'Doc' had helped her tremendously. I firmly believe that.

The minute I saw 'Doc,' my life changed right then and there! He was my first hero who started to reverse this depressing saga of total helplessness and despair into a tale of hope and wellness.

'Doc' is a holistic chiropractor who treats the whole body, not just the area which is causing problems. He follows the path of the nerves that are causing the problem in the body. If your wrist is hurting, he wants to find the root cause and treat that area as well as the wrist. At that fair, he told me that he thought he would be able to help me and to see him in his office as soon as I could.

Well, since numerous surgeries and extensive physical therapy sessions had not helped me in the least, I thought that I had nothing to lose by seeing him. I began treatments three times a week on my right knee. I was very diligent in doing my exercises at home and began to think that maybe this might just do some good.

He worked on my knee and, after a few months of treatment, I was able to take a few steps here and there without pain—the first time in twenty years! Seeing continued improvement down the road, I threw away my cane and I've never picked it up again!

Doc is so non-judgmental that I began to slowly tell him of my 'crazy' symptoms. He was especially concerned about my balance issues. After numerous discussions on the subject, he began to strongly insist that I have an MRI of my brain to try to figure out why my balance was so poor.

At first, I resisted, because over the years, the few doctors in whom I had confided had convinced me that nothing significant would ever be found. I had come to the steadfast belief that I was just weak and feeble and that the problem was all my fault. Besides that, I was almost 60 years old at that time, why bother? It was too late to make any changes in my life now. It wouldn't make any difference. My life was nearly finished–at least, I hoped that my life was pretty much over. *Enough is enough!*

Doc really started to pressure me into having the test. "What harm will it do?" he asked. *It will again prove that there's nothing wrong with me!* I answered in my mind's eye. Since my knee was actually starting to feel better, I decided to go ahead with the test, really just to placate him. *It will be a waste of time,* I thought, but I didn't want to jeopardize my relationship with him. I knew that I needed him to continue working on my knee. But I was sure that this test would also show absolutely nothing abnormal and that it would prove yet again that I was just incredibly weak and clumsy.

CHAPTER 24

The Test That Saved My Sanity and Changed My Life!

In October of 2007, I went to *Baystate Medical Center* in Springfield, Massachusetts to have the MRI of my brain. I jokingly said, "Well, Dad always did say on numerous occasions that I should have my head examined!" I went home that day and didn't really give the test much further thought. I knew that it was going to prove once again that there was absolutely nothing wrong with me and that I was just imagining all of my weird symptoms. How wrong I was!

The day after I had the MRI, I was in Doc's office for my regular appointment for my knee treatment. He called my sister, who was also being treated by Doc, into the same treatment room. "Well, this is odd," we said. "Doc never treats us together."

Doc, looking very solemn and rather worried, informed us that the neurosurgeon at *Baystate Medical Center* wanted me to go the neurological emergency room <u>immediately</u>. My MRI was ***grossly abnormal*** and they were afraid that I had a ***glioma***, a cancerous brain tumor which was most likely malignant. They said that time was of the essence if this were true.

My sister looked absolutely panic-stricken but I was eerily calm. Once again, I balked and assured my sister and Doc that I had had these problems all my life. Although the symptoms had been getting progressively worse to a critical level, they were the same problems with which I had struggled all of my life. The one thing I <u>wasn't</u> concerned about was cancer. After all, I had been suffering for so many years that, if it were cancer, it would surely have killed me by now. At least I was correct in that assumption.

So, Barbara and I went home that day, knowing that perhaps now I would finally find a reason for my troubling lifelong problems. *There really is something wrong with me,* I thought gleefully. It felt as if I shouldn't be happy for that news but, truth be told, I was ecstatic!

CHAPTER 25

Finally, A Diagnosis!

We made an appointment to see Dr. Dennis Oh, neurosurgeon *extraordinaire* at *Baystate Medical Center*, the following day. He is the second hero in my life. The minute I saw his smiling face, I knew that I was in very good hands. And for once, I was so right!

Because of the possibly serious nature of my diagnosis, I wanted my sister to be with me when I spoke with him. When he greeted my sister and me at the door, he asked who the patient was. When I said that I was, he replied that, from the results of my MRI, he expected me to have to crawl in on my hands and knees!

Dr. Oh asked me to tell him all of my 'weird' symptoms. *Here we go again*, I thought. *Now I get to see that look of disbelief once again.* Wrong! Wrong!! Wrong!!! As I continued to relate my difficulties, that glorious smile of his grew even wider as he began nodding his head. Dr. Oh asked me to walk away from him and he said to my sister, "See how she's shuffling her feet? She's walking as if she's pushing a grocery cart. That is not a normal gait. And watch as she turns. She takes tiny steps as she shuffles her feet from side to side to make a complete circle."

He asked me if I tended to trip with one particular foot. I replied, "Yes, it always seems to be the right foot. That's why my right knee is so badly messed up."

With a huge grin, he knew that my signs and symptoms definitely matched the results of my MRI. He told me that the test showed **marked *hydrocephalus*** (water on the brain), probably from **birth**! He could not believe that I had gotten through this much of my life with so much fluid on the brain. "How could you possibly have functioned at all?!" he exclaimed. *It wasn't easy*, I thought. "I don't know how you were even able to get out of bed!" he stated.

There are actually parts of my skull that are very thin and fragile due to the pressure of all that fluid pressing against the bone all those years. Who knew??!! Certainly not that country doctor from my childhood. But I can't fault him. He had no way of testing for something as obscure as hydrocephalus in a young child. *Don't worry, Dr. K. All is forgiven.*

Back in my neurosurgeon's office, Dr. Oh smiled that beatific smile of his and explained, "You have been troubled by all of these problems because your duct is blocked on the right side. There are ducts on both sides of the brain that draw cerebrospinal fluid away from the brain. In a normal person, the ducts on both sides of the skull perform this function well."

The duct on the left side of my skull functioned normally which is how I was able to function at all. However, the duct on the right side was clogged and would only allow the fluid to drain occasionally. When the duct was not functioning properly, I would suddenly fall and not be able to get up off the floor or I would feel that miserable sensation in my head. It caused those moments when I felt as if I was listening to someone speaking to me in a foreign language. It was because the duct on my right side was obstructed that caused me to always trip with my right foot! And my poor right knee suffered the consequences throughout my entire lifetime!

To Dr. Oh, it all seemed so obvious but to me, it was like a light bulb finally lit up in my brain. Oh, what a wonderful day that was! *There really is something wrong with me! Hallelujah! Someone finally figured it out!*

Dr. Oh said that I could have a shunt implanted in my skull to drain and regulate the flow of cerebrospinal fluid from my brain. He cautioned me, however, that since I had had this problem all my life, he wasn't sure if it would help at all. The procedure had been very successful in children with the condition but there were relatively few adults who had undergone the procedure.

I made the comment to Dr. Oh that I had thought all my life that I was just extremely weak and clumsy. He smiled and very kindly said, "No, Jeanne, that was all due to this condition. You are not clumsy. There was no way you could have prevented all those falls. It wasn't your fault!" I remember that I began crying with relief at that point. And you know what? I wasn't even embarrassed when the tears flowed openly down my cheeks ….. Dr. Oh grabbed my hand and said, "It's okay. We can most likely fix this."

Dr. Oh asked me to think very carefully if I wanted to go through with the shunt procedure since there was no guarantee that it would help at all. But whether or not it would help didn't matter so much at that particular moment. I breathed a sigh of relief and thought, *So, I wasn't just being a feeble crybaby, after all! There really was something wrong with me all these years! That doctor in my childhood was very, very wrong!*

I was to have a repeat MRI in a few months and we would make the decision about surgery then. Dr. Oh wanted to allow some time to pass to see if the condition cleared.

We both knew very well that it wouldn't but that was proper medical protocol.

I left Dr. Oh's office that day with a huge smile on my face. My grin was almost as big as the smile on Dr. Oh's face! It's amazing that being told you need brain surgery could be such a source of jubilation and relief!

Oh, yeah, Barbara and I went home and we certainly celebrated that night! *Woo-Hoo!! There's something wrong with me! It's finally there in undeniable black and white! No more looks of disbelief for me!*

CHAPTER 26

Learning About the Condition

When my sister and I got home from my initial consultation that day, I went to the internet and started researching hydrocephalus. I kept saying, *That's me! That's exactly what happens to me!! I have that problem too! Every problem I have is from this one condition!* It was such a relief to have all those seemingly unrelated signs and symptoms finally brought out into the open under one diagnosis!

I learned that hydrocephalus causes:

memory loss
speech problems
apathy
withdrawal
changes in behavior or mood
difficulty with reasoning, paying
    attention, or judgment
unsteadiness
leg weakness
sudden falls
shuffling steps with wide-based gait
difficulty taking the first step as
    if foot is stuck to the floor

urinary urgency and incontinence

headaches

nausea

difficulty focusing eyes

I had suffered from <u>every one</u> of these signs and symptoms throughout my life. No wonder existence for me had been so miserable.

I felt as if the weight of the world had finally been lifted from my shoulders. Even if I decided not to have the operation or if the operation didn't work, it was such a wonderful feeling to know that there had been a very real medical cause for all of the misery in my lifetime. I wasn't just imagining it and I certainly wasn't just a weakling.

I remember that at Christmas, I wrote on everyone's card, "Guess what?! I need brain surgery!" Boy, did that get everyone's attention! After the initial panic was over, I calmly explained that it was a very good thing, a very good thing indeed! Since no one had known about my 'condition', it came as quite a shock to everyone. But I was SO happy! There was now concrete proof that I wasn't just imagining anything. What a wonderful Christmas that was!

Barbara and I discussed the pros and cons of having the surgery. After some very careful thinking, I came to the conclusion that I had nothing to lose by having the operation and possibly everything to gain. I informed Dr. Oh of my decision but he still wanted to wait until early spring to give me more time to consider my decision. We agreed that I would proceed with the repeat MRI as previously scheduled for the spring and that we would discuss possible surgery at that later time. So, I sat back and bided my time through that cold and snowy winter–the winter of my *content,* not my *discontent* (Get it?!)

CHAPTER 27

A Gifted Man

N ow for an explanation of the title for my memoir -
After I had been diagnosed with hydrocephalus,
a television show, *A Gifted Man*, caught my attention.
The premise of the show revolved around a very talented
neurosurgeon (read–Dr. Oh) whose social worker wife had
been killed by a hit and run driver. Her spirit comes to Dr.
Michael Holt and he struggles to keep her visitations a secret
from those around him. I enjoyed that type of story line and
so I began to watch it faithfully.

In one episode, Dr. Holt visits one of his wife's former
clients who has become a recluse. She is showing serious signs
of dementia, talking to people who aren't there, tripping
constantly, and displaying signs of extreme paranoia. Dr.
Holt gets her to his very exclusive hospital as he ponders
her condition. It became obvious that she suffered from
severe urinary incontinence. He struggled to come up with
a diagnosis. Then he suddenly snapped his fingers and said,
"She's wacky, wet, and wobbly! She has hydrocephalus!" Well,
let me tell you, my ears perked right up at that pronouncement.

He did a spinal tap which temporarily relieved the pressure of the cerebrospinal fluid on her brain. I don't remember how the episode ended. I think she refused further surgery and returned to her previous paranoia and dementia. But I got a nifty title for my memoir out of the episode!

CHAPTER 28

Star Trek, Revisited

Since I was feeling more optimistic about my life, I decided to put those months of waiting to good use. I took that very brief **Star Trek** novel off the shelf, dusted it off, and began rewriting it. I now had a whole life's worth of experiences from which to draw. After all, they say that one of the things you should do in retirement is to write a book, right? I found that I felt safe sitting in front of the computer and didn't have to fear falling while I was writing. So writing was and still is a good outlet for me. It's so empowering to be able to create something out of thin air. I found myself getting lost in thought as to what I could have my characters encounter.

I remember writing a chapter and then rereading it. I thought, "Well, that was pretty boring. What can I do to spice it up?" After giving it considerable thought, I said, "I know, I'll set the Bridge on fire!" When you're really into writing, it's amazing how liberating it is to know exactly how your characters would react in a certain situation. The characters, as well as all of us, are more or less programmed by our surroundings and environment to behave in characteristic manners. The fun part is making those circumstances stretch the reaction of your character but still be within the confines of their personalities.

Since the original version of my book was very short, I developed the main plot line, my major character, added several side plots, and put together a very compelling full-length (117,250 words) novel entitled *What Price, Pantropy?* (Cool title, huh? Doesn't it just make you want to read the book?!) If you are a fan of *Star Trek: The Original Series*, I assure you that you would not be disappointed.

I could hear in my mind Chekhov's Russian accent and Scotty's Scottish brogue. The way I have written their words, you'd swear that you were hearing them too!

Since <u>Simon and Schuster</u>, a subsidiary of **CBS Corporation**, holds the copyright on that subject matter, they are the only ones who can officially publish *Star Trek* novels. They will only consider novels that are 'pitched' to them through a literary agent. With that in mind, I began searching for an agent.

I scoured books on how to go about procuring an agent. I wrote to <u>Simon and Schuster</u>, asking them to consider my book without going through an agent. I never heard back from them. Several follow-up letters also warranted no reply.

Whenever I saw an agent's name listed in a book, I wrote to that agent, begging them to consider taking me on. Again, if I got any response at all, it was to say "Sorry. This is not the right project for me."

Years ago, when I worked on the beginnings of *Pantropy*, I had contacted a *Star Trek* author. He was probably the only one who actually wrote back to me. He told me to simply enjoy writing for the pure pleasure of it but that it was nearly impossible for an unknown *Star Trek* author to be published by <u>Simon and Schuster</u>. How right he was! It's the same old story: You can't get the job because you don't have the experience and you can't get the experience because you can't get the job! I contacted this author again after I had finished rewriting *Pantropy* years later. His advice remained the same–enjoy writing but I should save myself the pain of trying to have it published. I even asked him if he would ask his own agent to look at my work but he said that his agent is no longer in the business. I then offered to have this known author 'ghost-write' for me for half the profits but he still wasn't interested. His life now no longer included *Star Trek*.

Although rather discouraged at this point, I vowed that I would not give up without a Herculean effort. I know my books are good and I want *Star Trek* fans to enjoy them. With that in mind, I subscribed to the Literary Market Place to obtain the names of possible agents. I learned what agents look for in an inquiry letter. Some agents will only read snail mail, some will only do email without attachments. If you add an attachment to your email inquiry, they will immediately delete it without even opening it. I felt as if I had been sucked into a black hole in space! I spent many weeks copying sample chapters of my book(s) and sending them off to these elusive agents. The very few I heard from also said, "Sorry." The rejection letters were all form letters. I think only one agent actually wrote to me personally. She was very nice, although not interested, and encouraged me to keep trying. I began to wonder what these enigmatic agents actually do beside write rejection letters!

I discovered that Archway Printing is a self-publishing agency associated with Simon and Schuster. At this point, I was quite willing to pay $2000.00 to have my first book self-published. I was hopeful that if Simon and Schuster saw how well my first book sold, then perhaps they'd be anxious to pick up my two other books. (Oh, I guess I haven't yet mentioned at this point that I had written two more *Star Trek* books. Yeah, yeah. So I'm a glutton for punishment! Details to follow!)

Things were proceeding well with <u>Archway</u> until I once again asked if the copyright issue would be a problem. "Copyright? Your subject is copyrighted?" Suddenly, the whole project was ditched and I was thrown back down into that black hole in space.

Since I was becoming so frustrated about my inability to connect with a literary agent, I found myself putting all of my energy into writing my second *Star Trek* novel! Obviously, I just don't know when to quit! Well, that's pretty apparent in my refusal to give in to my condition all my life, whatever it was, right?

So I wrote *T'Khut Rising* (117,400 words). It's the sequel to the first novel and it is even more compelling than the first. (Another cool title, huh? You should read the book!) *But wait! There's more!* I decided that I would have to write a third novel to complete what I began thinking of as "The Joanna Trilogy". I have now completed work on *Plague!!!* (117,650 words). All three of my novels draw from the best of *Star Trek: The Original Series*. A true fan of the show would be able to close his eyes and just see and hear the characters and imagine the action. It's that authentic and true to the *Star Trek* premise.

I recently found a literary firm which had attempted to get an agent for me so that my books can be pitched to <u>Simon and Schuster</u>. The owner of the agency told me that his friend used to date Gene Roddenberry's daughter. He suggested that my book could be a very successful movie. (I know what you're thinking ..... *There's one born every minute.* Okay, okay, so that's me!) Anyway, they tried to find an agent for me and were also unsuccessful and so now I'm back to square one yet again. Lo and behold, Paramount Pictures hasn't come calling either. Oh, well, the thought made for some happy times. Although I don't know if professional publication is in the future for me, I haven't given up hope!

I'm usually pretty self-effacing but I know that my books are worthy of publication. If a literary agent is reading this missive, how about giving me a chance? We could go *"Where No Man Has Gone Before"*©. I assure you that it would be worth your while.

It seems only **logical** (*thank you, Spock!*) to me that <u>Simon and Schuster</u> should allow unknown but very talented **Star Trek** authors to self-publish through <u>Archway Publishing</u>, a subsidiary of <u>Simon and Schuster</u>. If only one publisher had this privilege, the integrity of the **Star Trek** franchise could be easily maintained. <u>Archway Publishing</u> would profit from this arrangement as I know that there are many unpublished and very frustrated **Star Trek** authors out there who would surely be willing to pay for the opportunity to self-publish their **Star Trek** manuscripts. It would be a win for <u>Archway</u>, a win for <u>Simon and Schuster</u>, and a win for those very talented **Star Trek** authors (like me!) who are eager to pay for the privilege of self-publishing their work. I know I would be at the head of that line!

Hey, <u>Simon and Schuster</u>, how about giving me a break and consider publishing my THREE novels? They've been proofed and are ready for the press. What have you got to lose?! All right, all right! So you have your rules but a girl can dream, can't she? But rules are made to be broken if the end result is worthwhile, right? So, how about it, <u>Simon and Schuster</u>? All I'm asking for is a chance to fulfill my lifelong dream ..... *These are the voyages of the Starship **Enterprise**.....* ©

CHAPTER 29

The Long-Awaited Surgery

I tend to digress when I'm speaking of **Star Trek** so I guess I should get back to my life-changing surgery.

In February of 2008, I had a Codman-Hakim Programmable valve (cerebral-abdominal shunt) inserted into my skull by Dr. Oh to slowly decrease the amount of cerebrospinal fluid in my brain. It drains the fluid into a catheter that runs down the side of my neck and into my stomach. From there, the fluid is excreted from my body.

I will admit that the surgery was not a piece of cake. When I woke up from the anesthesia, Dr. Oh was combing some kind of goop out of my hair. Of course, the back of my head had been shaved and I looked rather dazed. However, I was very optimistic that the operation would be a success. Like I said, I had nothing to lose.

I had to stay in the hospital overnight. Because Barbara had been at the hospital all day, I told her to go home and get some rest. The highlight of my afternoon was choosing what I wanted for my dinner. Even though I was rather bored, at least the surgery was over and I seemed to be no worse for wear (except for that icky goop in my hair).

With my head swathed in a bandage, I bid a fond farewell to the staff of *Baystate Medical*. I can't say that it was fun but they took excellent care of me. I was anxious to get home so I could get some rest. Hospitals are very noisy places, not exactly conducive to sleep. Did you know that they really <u>do</u> wake you up in the middle of the night to give you a sleeping pill? Incredible!!!

CHAPTER 30

Could It Be?!

A few days post-op, I practically flew up the stairs at home rather than slowly dragging myself up by using the banister, as I usually did. *Could I attribute that solely on the fact that my knee was so much better, thanks to Dr. Andosca?* I wondered. *Could the surgery have actually helped?* **Yes, Yes, Yes!** (*"I'll have what she's having ....."*) The effects of the surgery have been **<u>dramatic and life altering</u>**.

I feel twenty years younger, have so much energy, can rise from a chair or bed without the use of my arms (or two or three tries!), no longer suffer from urinary frequency and incontinence, my balance has become normal, I no longer trip over uneven surfaces or going UP the stairs (significant for hydrocephalus), no longer suffer from sudden falls, no longer have leg weakness. I walk at a normal pace (actually, my sister now frequently asks me to slow down!), no longer shuffle when I walk, and no longer fear falling. I'm more confident and sociable. In fact, I frequently stop to talk with total strangers on the street or in the supermarket. When Barbara asks me, "Who was that?" and I reply, "I don't know. I never saw him before," she just rolls her eyes, smiles, and shakes her head.

My checkbook is now balanced to the penny and I no longer feel overwhelmed. In fact, at the age of 58, I finally knew what it felt like to be **normal**! (Yeah, yeah, I know there are some people out there who would say that I could never be normal!)

There's a magnetic dial under my scalp where the doctor can adjust the flow of fluid draining from my brain. A few weeks after surgery, I started having those same horrible symptoms again and I'll admit that I panicked just a bit. I thought I'd have to go through the entire surgery all over again. Dr. Oh calmly said, "No, we'll just turn up the volume a little." *Turn up the volume?* I wondered. *What in the world does he mean by that??!!* With a magnetic wand-type instrument, the valve was adjusted so that more fluid would drain. This is a non-invasive procedure done right in the office as part of my regular check-up. My symptoms abated instantly and I have had no problem ever since that time. *How did someone ever figure that out?* I marveled. Even Bones McCoy, Chief Medical Officer of the *Enterprise*, would be most impressed by that ingenuity.

I would now only need to see Dr. Oh annually unless my previous symptoms happen to return. Life is now worth living! Yahoo!!!

CHAPTER 31

The Astonishing Results

When I went back to see Dr. Oh for my third annual check-up, I proudly told him that I had been doing *Zumba*, an exercise form based on Latin dance rhythms. I showed him how I was able to stand for many seconds on one foot without toppling over! He was most impressed and gratified. His face lit up into that wonderful smile of his.

I gratefully told him that he had changed my life. He very modestly said, "I do this operation all the time. It wasn't anything special." Well, it was surely very special to me. Not only is Dr. Oh the quintessential neurosurgeon, he is even more importantly one of the finest people I have ever met. Despite his amazing success, he remains humble and self-effacing. He treats each and every one of his patients so humanely, as if s/he is a beloved member of his own family. Whenever I say "Dr. Oh", I always follow it with, "I love that guy!" If every doctor was like him, the world would be a much better place.

After he had checked me over and we had chatted for a while, Dr. Oh's expression grew sad as he informed me that I was doing so well that he could no longer justify my coming back to see him for check-ups anymore. He gave me a big bear hug and we both shed a tear or two as we parted.

"Of course, if you start having any problems, don't hesitate to come back! You're always welcome here," he added. "But I hope you never have the need to see me again."

I am so grateful for all the changes that have occurred in my life as a consequence of the surgery. I think the astonishing results bear repeating: I walk at a normal pace now, no longer shuffle when I walk, and no longer fear falling. I can get up from a chair or bed without having to use my arms to push myself up. I can walk up the stairs without having to rely on the banister any longer to pull myself up. I'm more confident and sociable, and my checkbook is now balanced to the penny! I say hello to strangers on the street and smile a whole lot more now. It's funny that the slope in front of our home no longer looked scary at all anymore! All those fears have melted into the netherworld. I no longer suffer from urinary urgency and incontinence. I don't have to wear *Depends* anymore. Do you have any idea how liberating that is??!! Besides, those things are expensive but they certainly served their purpose. I don't know what I would have done without them. Since my surgery, I get up perhaps once during the night to urinate, not the five or six times a night prior to my surgery. And I certainly no longer have any incontinence of stool.

I feel like I have a purpose in life now. I can make a difference. I do have a right to breathe in the oxygen of our world. Barbara no longer panics when she hears a loud noise coming from my bedroom. She was always running in to see if I had landed on the floor once again. Not anymore! She no longer drops me off at the front of the mall and no longer feels the need to offer me her elbow to keep me on my feet. Barbara was set as free as I was. Nice feeling! I really owed her that .....

It truly is wonderful to feel normal. I have almost forgotten what it felt like when I tried to lie on my stomach. I have to admit that I really haven't even tried that. I had those feelings for fifty eight five years and that's a hard habit to change.

I could go on and on about all of the **dramatic changes** in my life! Life is now certainly worth living! As a matter of fact, I am determined now more than ever to have my three novels published before I die–which hopefully won't be for a long, long time! (Sorry, God, but I've changed my mind about wanting to die very soon! Please let me enjoy this newfound freedom and feeling of normalcy for a very long time!)

CHAPTER 32

My Life's Mission

Revisiting all those agonizing memories was extremely difficult for me. I hope that my story has proven interesting and informative. But there is another much more important reason for me to share my painful story with you. Believe me, it wasn't easy to admit to all those fears, thoughts, and pain. Having to relive all those miserable moments in my life was beyond upsetting. I found that I had to keep taking breaks in order to dispel the distress that dredging it all up brought to me.

Although my hydrocephalus was from *birth*, the same symptoms can present themselves in later life. The ducts that draw cerebrospinal fluid away from the brain can become clogged simply due to the aging process. Even though a person may not have had a problem in the past, *hydrocephalus* can rear its ugly head due to advanced age.

Some older people who have started to display memory problems and poor balance are being misdiagnosed as having either dementia or Parkinson's disease. Medical research has shown that some of these people are actually suffering from **adult-onset hydrocephalus** which can be easily diagnosed with an MRI with contrast. They could once again lead productive lives after the insertion of a shunt. However, many doctors do not think of this condition in adults but rather only in children.

I believe that there is a reason that God had given me this lifelong problem that was finally treated successfully. I know now that it is my responsibility to get the word out to people about this debilitating condition which is the reason that I have written this memoir. Believe me, reliving all these painful memories was not a fun way to spend my days. I feel compelled to tell my story in the hope that perhaps even one person who has been misdiagnosed could be helped out of this crippling situation.

To that end, I have sent emails and snail mail to every major news station, including *NBC Nightly News*, *CBS News*, and *ABC News*. I sent my information to our local news stations including *Channel 22 News*, *ABC 40 News*, *CBS News Springfield*, and *MASS Appeal*, a local news/entertainment show. I contacted our local newspapers including *The Republican* (Springfield) and the *Daily Hampshire Gazette*. I also sent information to *Readers Digest*, *Woman's World*, and *First for Women*.

The only agency that I heard from was the television show *Mystery Diagnosis*. They expressed an interest and I completed an extensive application form. The producer made arrangements to have the segment filmed at my home. As the date drew near, I hadn't heard from them and so I contacted them. My email and phone calls were never returned and I once again fell into that black hole of disappointment. That's a shame because I think that would have been the ideal vehicle for disseminating information on the condition.

I have written several articles that have been published locally and have given speeches detailing my journey. They were well-received and I felt as if I had done my small part in bringing this condition to the forefront of people's minds.

I hope that by publishing this memoir that perhaps a larger audience will be reached.

If you know of someone who has suddenly begun displaying some of the symptoms that I have described, please don't accept the off-handed diagnosis of Parkinson's disease or dementia.

I hope you'll urge that person to have an MRI of the brain with contrast. It could save that person and his or her family from years of needless suffering.

If just <u>one</u> person is helped by my story, then my years of suffering will not have been in vain.

Thank you for reading my story.

God bless you and those you love.

Jeanne G. DeBold
Misty1701@Yahoo.com

9 781643 673325